# Thoughts of a Hessian Officer

*On what has to be done during a Tour with a detachment in the Field*

By Johann Ewald
Translated and with an introduction by James R. Mc Intyre

Cover
*Thoughts of a Hessian Officer on What Has to Be Done During a Tour with a Detachment in the Field* by Johann Ewald
Translated by James McIntyre

This edition published in 2020

Published by Winged Hussar Publishing, LLC
1525 Hulse Road, Unit 1
Point Pleasant, NJ 08742

ISBN 978-1-950423-10-1 Hardcover
ISBN 978-1-950423-37-8 ebook

Bibliographical References and Index
1. History. 2. Military Science. 3. 18th Century



For more information on Winged Hussar Publishing, LLC, visit us at:
https://www.wingedhussarpublishing.com

# Thoughts of a Hessian Officer

*On what has to be done during a Tour with a detachment in the Field*

By Johann Ewald

Translated and with an introduction by James R. Mc Intyre

# Contents of This Edition

# Introduction

Translating and editing an obscure military treatise from the eighteenth century may, at first glance, seem like a great waste of time. Even a peripheral examination of Johann (later von) Ewald's treatise, however, will disclose the significance of his work. Ewald's *Gedanken eines hessichen Officier uber das, was man bey Fuhrung eines Detaschements im Felde zu thun hat.* (*Thoughts of a Hessian officer about what he has to do when Leading a Detachment in the Field.*) is useful both as a part of the military side of the Enlightenment, and for his contribution to the growing use of light troops in Europe.[1] His treatise offers insights into eighteenth century European warfare from the perspective of tactical operations as well. In the spirit of the Enlightenment, Ewald is examining an aspect of war, the use of small units on detached service, and logically explaining how they can be put to the best use. When he wrote *Thoughts of a Hessian Officer*, he held the rank of lieutenant in the army of Hessen-Kassel, thus he provides the perspective of a relatively junior officer on the conduct of small war or *kleinen kreig.* In many regards, his work is similar to Jeney's *The Partisan.*[2] This translation, then, helps to further illuminate our understanding of what could be called best practices as they related to light troops. Concerning the use of light troops, from the War of the Austrian Succession (1740-1748) on, these troops underwent a renaissance of sorts in Europe.[3] Their use grew much more widespread during the Seven Years' War and proliferated out to the North American theater as well. The following treatise by Johann Ewald is therefore useful on several levels. In order to place this work in its full context, some description of the author's background is necessary.

The author of the following text, Johann Ewald, served in the Army of the Landgraf of Hesse-Cassel from 1760 until 1786. During that time, he participated in both the latter stages of the Seven Years' War and the American War of Independence. Born in the city of Kassel in the Marvgraviate of Hessen-Kassel on 30 March 1744, he grew up in a society in which military service stood as commonplace. Little is known about his youth. His father, Georg Heinrich Ewald, worked as a bookkeeper and his mother, Katherine Elisabeth Ewald née Breithaupt, was the daughter of a Kassel merchant.[4] Johann Ewald's roots, then, were planted firmly in the soil of the middling class. It is likely that his parents taught him to read, as it is clear he was literate from an early age.

Growing up during the eighteenth century in the center of Kassel, military service was as a relatively common vocation and one of the best possible avenues of social advancement likely fired the youth's imagination with dreams of martial glory. After all, the year Johann was born stood at the halfway point in the War of the Austrian Succession (1740-1748), a war in which Hessen-Kassel played a dubious role where they had troops actually serving on both sides.

Ewald's father died during his early childhood, leaving his mother as his only guardian. On her death, young Ewald was taken in by older relatives. His interest in the military continued to grow. Meanwhile, the fires of war once again burst over Europe and Hesse-Kassel found itself engrossed in a new European conflict—the Seven Years' War. Now in his early teens, Ewald's family made one final attempt to dissuade the youth from embracing a military career. His uncle took the young man to the battlefield of Sandershausen, fought on 23 July 1758, to witness the carnage that constitutes battles' aftermath firsthand. Rather than shrink in horror, the young Ewald supposedly cried out, “Oh, how happy are they who died for their country in such a way!”[5]

The youth’s driving ambition was to serve. Attempts to dissuade him from his aspiration ceased soon thereafter. It should come as no surprise that on 23 June 1760, at the age of 16, Ewald joined the Regiment von Gilsa. After joining the Regiment Gilsa, Ewald left from the gates of Cassel at dawn on the following day.[6] As his son Carl later noted in a biography of his father, the young Johann Ewald waited at the city gates with “the calm of a veteran.”[7] Soon he arrived at the regimental bivouac at Neustadt the following day.[8] The line infantry regiments of the Hessian army consisted of single battalion units. The terms regiment and battalion will therefore be used interchangeably in describing the Hessian infantry formations of the Seven Years’ War. Each battalion held ten companies, giving a total of 770 men.[9]

The younger Ewald would later paint a vivid picture of his father’s early days serving in the unit and the discomforts of his new military life, “In the ranks of the Hessian Regiment von Gilsa marched 16-year-old *Freikorporal* Johannes Ewald, whose weary feet could hardly move forward, weighed down by the heavy, chunky musket on his shoulder, which, with the intersecting bandoliers on his chest, left the boy hardly able to breathe.”[10] His description presents an image to which anyone who has endured military basic training can relate. His designation as *freikorporal* meant that Ewald was essentially a gentleman volunteer, or someone who was serving unattached to any unit until a junior officer’s billet could be found for them.[11] Summing up his father’s experience, he observed, “It was a hard school, which he had chosen, more than once it was with teeth clenched against loosing heart that he marched on.”[12]

Ewald did not keep any thorough record of his experiences in the war which has survived. It does seem likely, however, that he kept some record as when he wrote his first treatise some years after the conflict, he referenced specific engagements in which he took part

The Grenadier Regiments of von Rall of Hesse-Kassel and Sprecht of Brunswick as well as Officers of the Field Jäger Corps of Hesse-Kassel while serving with the Regiment von Gilsa. What follows is a reconstruction of his involvement based on several sources.[13] The first step in the young Ewald's indoctrination into the army involved providing him with a uniform.[14]

Since the command and the designation of the regiment recently changed, their uniform had as well. In his biography of Johann Ewald, his son Carl emphasizes that his father was provided with a new uniform. This is significant in that the new uniform may not as yet have been in great supply. The new uniform consisted of a blue coat with black cuffs and facings and red turnback. The britches were buff.[15] Proper attire was important as Ewald was considered something of a junior officer, and therefore had to look the part. Ewald was initially assigned to Major von Keudel's company, in which a Lieutenant Schlemmer took the new recruit under his wing.[16] In such a practice, a more experienced junior officer taking a new volunteer under his tutelage was prevalent in early modern armies as well.

The campaign of 1760 officially began on June 22, when the French Army under Marshal Broglie began to march on the town Giessen. Ewald would not have long to wait for his first taste of combat. It is highly likely that the recruit witnessed the battle of Korbach, fought on 10 July 1760. Lieutenant Schlemmer ordered the young man to remain the baggage during battles until he was fully trained. It is therefore unlikely that Ewald played any direct role in the fighting at Korbach, which stood as Hessian loss.[17]

Several days later, on 16 July, the Hessians gained a chance for revenge as they caught the French army sitting down to lunch at Emsdorf and inflicted a tactical defeat on them. While it was likely that Ewald witnessed the battle, given his status as a raw recruit, Schlemmer probably kept him out of this combat as well. Still, the young soldier's determination to take his place in the impressed his superiors.[18]

The next major engagement in which Ewald's regiment participated occurred at Warburg on 31 July 1760. The clash came about as the result of a series of maneuvers in which both Ferdinand and his French opponents sought to gain some advantage in the theater through movement as opposed to a direct clash of arms. In the end, the French lost fifteen hundred men to the allies twelve hundred. More indicative of the magnitude of their defeat, they lost twelve hundred prisoners and ten guns. Warburg, however, only stood as a tactical win for Ferdinand. He was unable to exploit the victory further since on the same day, Prince Xaver of Saxony and Lusatia captured Kassel when its small corps of defenders (eleven thousand men) under the command of Gen. Georg Ludwig von Kielmannsegg abandoned the city, which was important as a supply depot for Ferdinand's troops. The next day, Prince Xaver captured Münden, thus completing the conquest of Hessen.[19] After some additional clashes, Xaver managed to open the way to Hanover, but Broglie was unable to exploit this due to logistical difficulties. The result of this impasse was that for over a month, both forces remained idle. During this time, young Ewald may have completed some additional training. More importantly, he witnessed several engagements and likely had direct experience of combat. In the autumn of 1760, several minor engagements occurred in which Ewald may or may not have taken part. Then the army went into winter quarters.

The respite did not last long, as Ferdinand decided to open the campaign of 1761 with a winter campaign beginning on 9 February. His goal was to clear the French from Hessen-Kassel, Ewald's home state. During this stage of the campaign, one engagement in particular seems to have stuck in Ewald's memory, the assault on the city of Kassel on the night 6-7 March 1761. Strategically, Cassel, the capital of Hesse-Kassel, held great importance for Allied army. Likewise, it probably held some special significance for Ewald himself as it was his birthplace. In any case, his son describes Ewald's being chilled to the bone in the siege trenches as the troops got into position.[20] Before the Hessian assault troops got into their position, they were surprised by a sudden attack by the French garrison. Their assault threw back the Hessian and Hanoverian troops. The Hessians only restored their equilibrium when General von Gilsa himself assumed command. The Count von Schaumburg-Lippe led the overall counterattack.[21] An intense clash developed between the two forces. There were many wounded on the Hessian side, including Freikorporal Ewald, who received a musket ball through the thigh. Due to the seriousness of his wound, he was admitted to the main hospital at Iringhausen.[22]

The last engagement of the Seven Years' War Ewald fought in was that of Brücker Muhle or Amöneburg on 21 September 1762. It was the last battle of the war in the western theater as well. Further, it exerted a profound influence on Ewald, as he mentions it several times in his *Thoughts*. The clash came about as a result of Ferdinand's attempt to unite his dispersed formations and force an engagement with a portion of the French army under favorable circumstances to attack. The larger strategic goal was, to drive the French back across the Rhine and deny them any territorial bargaining chips in the German states. These territories could potentially be utilized as bargaining chips in ongoing negotiations in order to achieve the return of at least some of their overseas empire.[23] Unfortunately for Ferdinand, his French adversaries managed to both thwart his plans and achieve a union of their forces.

The terrain in which the battle was fought was a small mountain which rises out of a plain amidst several river crossings. There were a number of villages in the area, and a castle atop the mountain as well. Its battlements, however, do not seem to have been modernized at the time of the battle and may have dated back to the Middle Ages.

The French began the engagement with a bombardment of the city which commenced at 5 am on 21

September. Soon after the preparatory bombardment, they launched an infantry assault against Ferdinand's position. The assault broke down, however, as it encountered heavy resistance. As he received information on the hard fighting in this sector of the field, Ferdinand dispatched guns from his own artillery reserve to bolster the pieces in this area. Over the next few hours, the French launched a series of additional assaults against this part of the line, however, these were broken up with heavy artillery fire.[24] Interestingly, at this point during the battle, the French infantry units were given permission to advance in open order, to reduce their casualties from enemy fire.[25] It is interesting to speculate, given Ewald's subsequent career, whether he observed this movement during the battle, and if so, what impression it had on his fertile mind.

To maintain the pressure on the French during the afternoon, Ferdinand dispatched six more Hessian 12-pounders to provide additional fire support. The fighting was so intense that these guns ran out of ammunition and had to be replaced with a battery of Hanoverian 12-pounders.

Towards the late afternoon, the French redirected their efforts at the hills behind the bridge leading into the town. The regiments von Gilsa and von der Marlsburg occupied this section of the battlefield. Ewald and his unit were about the feel the full weight of the final French assault! The fighting died down in the early evening, but the battle was far from over. Both sides planned to rejoin the contest the following day.

The action began at roughly seven in the morning, with the French columns advancing rapidly on the allied positions. Heavy firing ensued on both sides as a desperate struggle erupted for control of that portion of the field. The fighting only broke off with the coming of night roughly an hour later. Ewald reported that the fighting over the hill occupied by his regiment was so intense, "The parapet on the hill was so shaved by cannon fire, that if one stood up, it would not cover them above the knee." He went on to record how the men used the bodies of the fallen to create an improvised barrier to protect themselves from the fire of their assailants.[26] This was during the defense of the Brücker Mühle, a post which the Allied army sent reinforcements to in various detachments. The fighting was so intense, Ewald would later describe it in his first treatise, "The hill was only held with a hundred men, who were replaced every half an hour."[27] He noted as well how a great effort was made to exhort the von Dittfurth and von Knyphausen Regiments to fight bravely as the men of these units moved in to defend the position. Confirming his experience, Ewald stated "I myself was witness to this murder-hole."[28] Clearly, for the young officer, this was an intense fight.

In a battle which lasted for roughly fourteen hours, the resulting casualties were surprisingly light. The Allied army lost roughly 745 killed and wounded, while the French sustained 350 killed and 730 wounded. On the French side, the marshal De Castries himself was among those wounded. The disproportion between the killed and wounded testifies in some measure to the ferocity of the fighting in this engagement.[29]

On the following day, September 22, the French renewed their assaults. In the ensuing fight the French succeeded in gaining the castle of Amöneburg and driving off the garrison.[30] While the French and Saxons had gained some key positions, the battle is usually seen as constituting a victory for Ferdinand's forces.[31] It was the last engagement in the western European theater of the Seven Years' War.

Following the end of hostilities, Ewald remained in army Hessen-Kassel, even as the Landgraf reduced the size of his forces for economic reasons. Ewald was posted to the garrison at Ziegenhain.[32] Peace brought financial hardship for Ewald since unnecessary officers had their pay cut. He later described how he, "Lay down some nights hungry to bed and spent the winter without fire in the stove..."[33] One night, in 1770, Ewald and a group of his peers went out for a night of conviviality. Soon, an argument broke out which led to a duel between Ewald and another officer. The two men fought a duel, in which Ewald lost his left eye and was nearly killed.

Following his recovery, which kept him down for some time, Ewald was sent to the Collegium Carolinium. While studying at the Collegium that Ewald composed the treatise, *Gedanken* or *Thoughts.* Ewald wrote *Thoughts* while studying under a professor Jakob Mauvillon (1743-1794) who taught economics and military theory at the Collegium at the same time Ewald attended the institution.

One of the interesting facets of the treatise is Ewald's style. He will outline a problem, for example the defense of a village. He would then present solutions to the problem derived from his reading of various military writers. In advocating a certain approach to a problem, Ewald would support the ideas of the other writers with his own experiences in the Seven Years' War. It is clear that during his time at the Collegium, or perhaps during his long recovery from the duel, that Ewald read a wide variety of military authors. Not only did he draw supporting ideas from recent writers, such a Turpin de Crisse, La Cointe, and Jenny but he notes some classical authors as well.[34]

Though Ewald supplements the principles enunciated by these authors with examples from his own recent military experiences. It was his ability to bring together ideas from the works of other writers and provide real-life examples to support their ideas which separates his work from that of other military authors of the day.

Throughout Thoughts, it is evident that Ewald perceived war as more of a science than an art. This helped to firmly situate his work in the Military Enlightenment, an aspect of which involved the notion that war, like other human endeavors, could be studied logically, and a system for its conduct devised.[35]

Ewald's Thoughts received a warm reception, at least within Hessen-Cassel. The Landgraf gave it his approbation. It had more concrete benefits for Ewald as well, he was promoted to captain and transferred to the elite Jäger Corps. While there is no written evidence connecting the publication of his treatise with his promotion and transfer, the circumstantial case is fairly strong. The promotion followed shortly after the publication of the work. The Jägers were the type of troops that would most often serve in a detached role form a main force. They acted as scouts for the main force. It therefore seems plausible, that the Landgraf, who took a serious interest in military matters, read Ewald's treatise and determined that his service would be best rendered as a member of the Feld Jäger Corps.

Ewald served with this unit throughout the American War of Independence. Starting in 1776, he took part in the battles of Fort Washington as well as the pursuit through New Jersey. In 1777, Ewald served at Brandywine, had advanced notice of the American attack on Germantown, took part in the attack on Fort Mercer, and finally went into winter quarters. He served in the fighting around Monmouth Courthouse the following year, and in the war of posts around New York City. He later served at the siege of Charleston in 1781 and was with Earl Charles Cornwallis when the British commander surrendered at Yorktown.

Ewald's story does not end in Virginia, however. Following the conclusion of the fighting in North America, he returned to Hessen-Kassel, and continued to serve the Landgraf faithfully for several more years. He also took up his pen once again and began to distil the lessons of his combat experiences in North America. His experiences spawned a number of works, the most significant of which was his Belehrunger uber den Kreig, besonders uber den kleinen Krieg, durch Beispiele grosser Helden und kluger und tapferer Manner, first published Schleswig in 1798. Later, this work was translated at a Treatise on Partisan Warfare.

In its native German, Ewald's Treatise found a more receptive audience in no less a military thinker than Carl von Clausewitz. During his time as a lecturer at the

*Mounted Jaeger* *Foot Jaeger*

Hesse-Cassel Field Jaeger Corps, 1776-1783

Hesse-Cassel Jägers according to Knötel, 1776 - 1783

Kriegs Academie, Clausewitz utilized Ewald's Treatise for his lectures on *kleinen krieg.* Clausewitz appreciated Ewald's work and singled it out for notice in his second lecture on the subject due to its numerous examples drawn from the author's own experiences.[36]

As noted above, the English translation of Ewald led to his ideas exerting a profound influence on the development of the British light infantry in the Peninsular War. Thus, it exercised some effect beyond the borders of Hessen-Kassel. Likewise, this is the version most likely consulted by J.F.C. Fuller in the early twentieth century.

Ewald produced a number of other military works in his later years as well. These included: *Gesprache eines Husarencorporals, eines Jagers und liechten Infanteristen uber die Pflichten und den Dienst der liechten Soldaten*, published in Altona in 1794 and *Belehrunger uber den Kreig, besonders uber den kleinen Krieg, durch Beispiele grosser Helden und kluger und tapferer Manner*, published in Schleswig in 1798. In addition, there was a second edition of his *Abhandlung von dem Deinst der Leichten Truppen* published in 1796.[37] Ewald supervised the transcription of his Diary of the American War from the notebooks he had kept while on service in North America as well.[38]

He later married and switched to the Danish service where he earned a patent of nobility and added "von" to his surname. Ewald served Denmark throughout the period of the French revolution and Napoleonic Wars. In this capacity, he helped to put down the uprising of Major Ferdinand von Schill against the French. He narrowly avoided being called into service for the disastrous Russia campaign as Denmark at the time stood as an ally of France. He died of dropsy on 25 June 1813 in Kiel, surrounded by his family. His gravesite was destroyed by allied bombing during World War II.

Johann von Ewald possessed a significant experience of war coupled with a keen inquiring mind throughout his life. These factors combined in the soldier-intellectual and allowed him to produce a number of works which influenced contemporaries. For the first time in English, here is his earliest published work. Hopefully this translation will allow other scholars to gain insights from a tactical-level participant in eighteenth century warfare, as well as the Military Enlightenment.

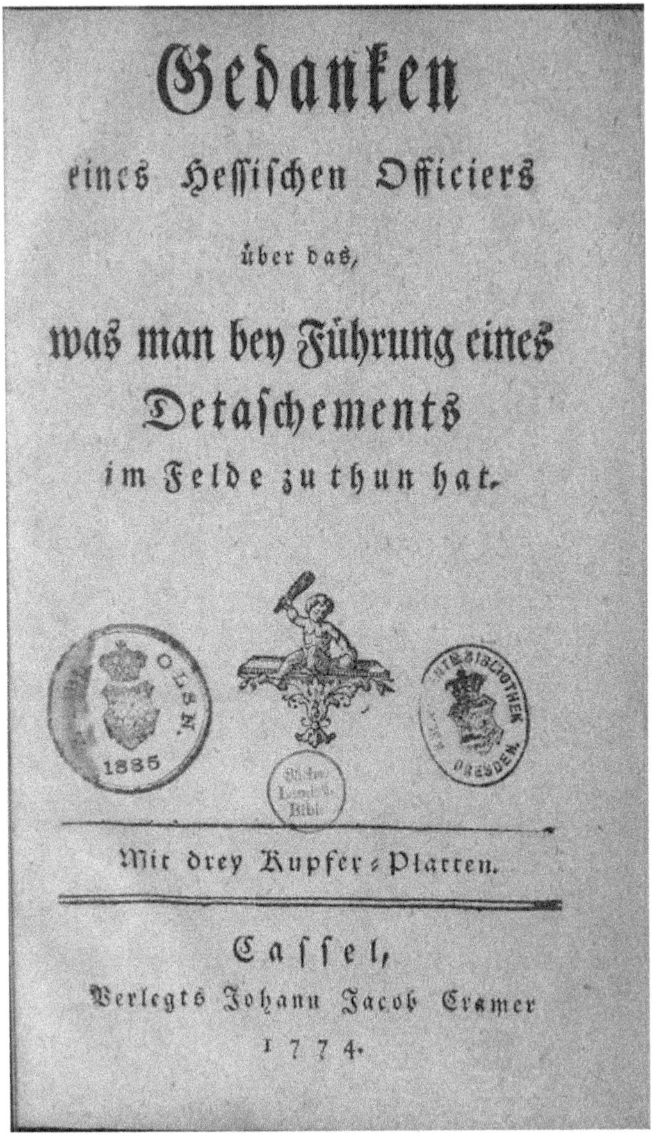

Gedanken
eines Hessischen Officiers
über das,
was man bey Führung eines
Detaschements
im Felde zu thun hat.

Mit drey Kupfer-Platten.

Cassel,
Verlegts Johann Jacob Cramer
1774.

Cover of the original work

## Dedicated to his Highness the Landgraf. Most Gracious Prince and Lord!

Your Princely Highness! This little effort from my studies and experience is here laid at your feet. I would not have dared to glimpse at the heights to which the manuscript has risen by your giving it your permission to be printed. Your Princely Highness is wealthier in the world than many, and possesses many sublime characteristics, a connoisseur of all sciences. Your Highness is a true protector of all who dedicate themselves to the sciences and can be assured that I do not undertake this bold step ungraciously.

The desire to become known as a writer, did not place the pen in my hand. Nor did a vain wish to see my name printed or to acquire a new post; No, it was probably all of my hours of studies that served as the engine that gave me my thoughts and the desire to write them down. And the grace of my high first theories called me to hope that I might have these few leaves carried to print. I very much hope the reader will see that I have no desire for glory.

Instead, full of true zeal, my entire life, I dedicate to the glorious service of your most princely Highness until my bones blow dry in death.

Your Princely Highness
Kassel, the 12th November 1773.

# Preface

Since man first encountered the dangers of war, a deceptive prejudice has developed, as if it is only through being in war itself that one can learn. To a larger extent, in this century, many people have enlightened us and delivered the finest works on the science of war into the hands of men. They have excelled at accommodating us with a systematic knowledge of the prosecution of war. They have started us on the way, to see the art of war as a science.

In his writings Count Puysegur showed us what you can learn in war. Out of many of those great men who have written on war he is by himself in thought, more often than not he made a broad start on the matter, as if drawn to correct the very weak abilities of novices.[39] The majority of writers have given little care to the first lessons for young officers and written only for the generals.

Turpin has indeed shown, in the pages of his compact writings, in which you can find in the rough some correct ideas among a number of incorrect ones. At the same time, he demonstrates how an officer accustomed to the infantry alone can handle only the movements of a detachment of five to six hundred men.[40]

The seignior le Cointe, captain of a dragoon regiment in the service of the King of France, is so to speak, the only true practitioner of petite guerre, who is included here.[41] In his writings he states his desire to explain the use of light troops in a detachment. He describes how to make the successful retreat of ten thousand and made the most instructive remarks. His book on the attack and defense of field posts demonstrates its utility from the outset and should be in everyman's hands. In ten books, this officer provides some of the best instruction on the use of detached troops. It is a pity that it is so powerful, but remains only available in French, and has not been translated into German so that it could be read more generally.[42]

We know from history that the greatest generals, before they rose to command, were accomplished at partisan tactics; and even Henry the Great, King of France, especially when he was still the prince of Navarre, was forced by circumstance to employ these tactics.[43] Without going so far back into the past; anyone who has taken part in the war of posts will understand its tactics. Salsbury probably seized on this part of war.[44] So did his princely highness, the hereditary Prince of Brunswick-Lüneburg, who is the most brilliant example in the world of the mind-set examined herein. Other great practitioners include Luckner, Freitag, Fischer and Scheiter.[45] In his remarks about Polybius, the Marquis de Folard says he owes his insights and much of his knowledge of military science to this aspect of warfare.[46]

But the majority of writers believe those who lead light troops do so unwillingly. They believe such troops are not needed in war. Did they not see the final campaigns of the last war when the allied army took volunteers from the regular troops, one battalion of which was formed under the name of Chasseurs. This was given to Major Rall to lead in the local service.[47]

Is it good enough to know that those of this battalion have been raised and not make known how this sort of war is conducted? It may be possible to know that similar cases occur in every war. The events in the War of the Austrian Succession show us that detachments from the main army call for the use of the light troops, and this commonly happens to start such a swarm of the light troops in war to the point where a man rarely sees the end.

It is sad that no training is offered for the officer of the infantry who must lead the advanced or rear-guard. Such an officer, who is not practiced in this activity, has not experienced its dangers, can easily, through his ignorance, fall into a situation in which he would lose his honor.

Thirteen years of service and years of contemplating all the ways that science impacts war, has provided me with some knowledge of the preferred manner of service in the field. I understand that service and have developed my own ideas. The following draws on the best lessons I can from my own experiences in order to instruct others.

I share this little study, divided into ten chapters, to show how an officer of the infantry should behave when he is on detached service in the field. Some have learned from good teachers and experience on campaigns to know as well as I do. Some know even more than I am delivering in this little study. If they would be so kind and understand that I am not writing for them. Instead, I am writing for those who lack the opportunity of a sufficient time to gain such knowledge. Others, however, who believe that their level of knowledge is already superior, feel free not to read this work.

My readers, incidentally, will have to be indulgent with my style. I am a soldier, and as such, I've had no leisure to put on melodious tones of eloquence. Where I myself am wrong or not clearly enough printed, I'm going where connoisseurs of military science see connections. If they honor me with some improvement, or anyway they condemn me, look at my previous reasons to hearten me and take up their ideas in a larger work.

# Contents of the Book

## Chapter One

*How an Officer of the Infantry Behaves When Leader of Detachments on the March.*

During the last war many examples occurred which were delivered into our hands wherein an officer must act according to his insights alone. Sometimes circumstances arise in which a post has to be possessed in order to make the march of a column safe. Likewise, patrols must be made, or he has to lead the advanced or rear-guard of a detachment which must be kept safe. How is an officer who obtained neither by theory nor experience a knowledge in the science of war, not to be embarrassed? Because he behaves in war as in other sciences like other men; man should gain ground rules by thorough learning, and the purpose here is to make those, such as they are, complete.

I am not going to go into details as what the service is called by different armies, and what an officer has to do to disengage of those detachments or to fall back. For these things, every officer has his own predetermined set of rules. These are understood by the officers themselves. Just as it is that the officer, before he marched with his detachment, investigates his people, checks that their guns are charged, that they are in good shape, checks whether powder is fresh in the pan, whether the flints are well and firmly in set in the cock, and whether the cartridges in each man's pocket are in the proper order to be grasped quickly. Through experience I know these things are often badly handled and can be forgotten if the officer does not see to his work carefully enough.

If he has done all the above things, and begun the march of his detachment, he should ride to rendezvous with his men and ensure that his men remain in contact with one another regardless of how wide their order. He should ensure that they make no noise as well. This is especially so if he happens to pass villages, manner houses or comparable obstacles. If he attends to these things, be assured that he will have nothing to fear from the enemy on the march; he may indeed permit his men to march with their rifles inverted yet be sure they can see an order at a moment's notice.[48] We must be sure never to fire when you have an enemy who does not know of your presence.

An example of what I am talking about was seen in the last war when an officer of the Imperial Army, who was only a few hundred yards distant from his column, while on the march, was taken prisoner by a Prussian Hussar officer. The way this brave man was caught, by accidentally falling in line with the enemy, to which I humbly say, namely not to fall in with the enemy.

However, when an officer fears the enemy on his march; he marches too cautiously and carefully. He feels he must keep his men under his control at all times, having some men fifty paces forward and some of the soldiers connected along the length of march to cover various points. Based on this I must strictly recommend that you first search everything around you. Look around at all times so that nothing evades their eyes, and they should be aware of something they perceive to be in the least bit suspicious. Additionally, the leader of any detachment must report frequently so that the commander can take the measure of the situation accordingly. When we find ourselves near such places as villages, manner houses, mills or mountains, we must in every case send some man forward to question the residents about the enemy. But you should go through the area yourself. This is essential to gain information about its layout personally before you march your troops through them. Doing so one can find gorges, highways, depressions, forests, bushes or other places where the enemy can hide easily. It is therefore imperative that a commander of a detachment search for these points himself; because how many examples can be found that of a detachment that was lost by imprudence and ignorance of their officers? I could give many examples that would give proof of what I summarize here. From a few, you can draw very large lessons.

The Marshal von Schomberg, who commanded the French army in the Spanish war in 1664[49], was informed that fodder collected at Roussillon needed protection, so he allowed Falles to march a considerable detachment to the convoy to make sure that it got from Perpignan, and accordingly on to the village of St. Jean du Page. This village was an hour from Perpignan.[50] The detachment was posted on a hill near the road. The commander detached a lieutenant with thirty men to move forward and find a chapel, which was three hundred yards away from the main post. This chapel would serve as an advanced post. Schomberg commanded him to conceal himself, so that the lieutenant was completely overlooked for hours on the level ground of Boulon where the Spaniards were in the camp.

The enemy had to make their way by this level ground, if they wanted to take possession of the French convoy. From Boulon up to the two posts was a hollow in which the Spaniards, once they became aware of its existence, could sneak. The Lord Marshal of Schomberg had de Falles, who was still heading to the Garden House, called the Red House, to secure it in order to prepare for an attack. De Falles was ordered to address the concern of daily security. Schomberg commanded, that as soon as the enemy was discovered to light fires in order to notify the other units, and that these should remain alert, so that they could offer the best possible support.

A Spanish officer whom combined the best knowledge of the land and those posts penetrated through the hollow with forty riders under the cover of the night. They attacked the aforementioned lieutenant's detachment who were on foot the following morning near the

Capelle forest. The French officer was barely in the hollow way, when the unavoidable happened to him. He was ambushed and the Spaniards fell unexpectedly on him and all his people. The attack lasted until all of his men were either killed or wounded. The Spanish officer himself gave ten sabre cuts, and even added this foul language: "Teach them to do their duty better and familiarize them ahead of time with the places through which they will lead their soldiers."

This example demonstrates how necessary it is see that officers reconnoiter the places they will move through before the same fate befalls them. This is so especially in mountainous areas, where you can often see no more than fifty paces ahead. Because the light in these areas tends to conceal the enemy from you, as well as you from him, it is easy to be surprised if you are not on your guard. On the following pages are all the things you need to do when leading a detachment to prevent yourself from being surprised or found. Beware of these cautions lest you spend every moment in danger of being cut-off and attacked.

But if in spite of all these precautions if the squad you're in is ambushed; one must find a house, mill, chapel or another place where you can hold out in safety as quickly as possible, against the assaults of the enemy, looking to win. You must plug entrances, windows and other gaps well and as fast as possible, and then let the enemy get in position, and fearlessly await.

But we must in this case use powder sparingly, and not start firing too early or unnecessarily. The reasons for this are so obvious that it is not necessary to give them.[51] Therefore, it is quite possible that if a detached force is not too far from the main army, the enemy come to a definite scare by a like maneuver, and it is possible to attack them while they are withdrawing. But should it seem impossible because of the location of the enemy, to achieve such an advantage, all that remains is to withdrawal as quickly as possible and to do so in the best order. In this case, an officer has to act by fixing the locks of his men's weapons. The mountains of corpses that otherwise result will drive this message home.

## Chapter 2

*On the Construction of the Quadrangular Redoubts, and How such Posts are to be Secured.*

There are thousands of cases that occur in the field, which create a need for the construction of field works. An officer will often be sent with a detachment to cover a bridge, ford, canyon, basin or hollow. Because he cannot send all of his engineers, he must send a detachment to stabilize the works in the mountains. It is important for an officer given this task be diligent.

It greatly helps an officer when he seeks knowledge of the construction of the different types of field works in peacetime. However, it is not feasible to obtain a thorough knowledge of military engineering without learning geometry. This fact often deters the young officers from trying it. I encourage it and, if I can, point out the value an officer can gain, even if he is not an engineer, if he has a basic understanding of this science. But before I can turn to this purpose, I want to touch on the one case in which an officer must judge with exacting attention.

In the future, the officer must turn to the art of selecting the ground where he can place his entrenchments. He must locate and possess such places that the enemy could use to sneak up on him unobserved, for example a hollow, geological depressions, bushes and like places near his post. After he selects his post, the commander must restrict access to it by obstructing the transit ditch, which he can do by placing downed trees across it. This is the quickest method to seal off access to his post. Second, he has to look for some obvious heights which might produce unfavorable consequences when they are in the rear of our enemy. Thirdly, the works must be laid out so that a strong fire is brought against the place where the enemy comes from.

If this is the case, and you have to select the ground in accordance with these kinds of terrain near to the post. By doing so in that way you create several high banquettes, raised high enough to protect your soldiers and hide them from the enemy, for nothing makes a patrol more uneasy than if they are shot at from behind.[52] The lowest of the banquettes that you construct should be about two feet tall, but in order to allow soldiers space to move, they must be four feet wide. Second, care must be taken that the space below the post does not narrow, making the men stand as if they were standing on a parapet. Third, the wall has to be designed so that you know where the enemy is coming from, and so can give a strong fire against them.

Now that an officer has acted accordingly to defend these earthworks, so now he can proceed to work. Imagine you defeat his people in segments of four equal parts, with each man two feet or one step apart. But if the detachment is a thousand men or more, he should provide a tenth of his men, or at the very least one-sixth, to act as a reserve. If organized in this way; we can make a reserve, on which the sixth part of his men are counted, and which is withdrawn, before dividing his troops into four parts.

Then take a straw rope, or a line, mark off the steps or footsteps of the four sides and take a quadrangle (square). Insert a rod and pull the rope from b, c, d; The inner side of the brigade square, the height of which is calculated by the horizon, must be six feet; one and a half feet can be counted using the breadth of the footstool, which can be ejected from the interior of the entrenchment; after deducting the height of the banquette it remains four and a half feet high, which can be fired by a soldier. Then, erect on each side a vertical (perpendicular) line, as denoted in Nr. 2.[53] Then insert twelve feet or six steps from which you get the thickness of the parapet, which gives the thickness of the breastwork, and erect with the line to the prescribed to place the second quadrilateral from e to f, g, h, but this must run parallel with the first. One sitting on a vertical line which is denoted by Nr. 3, then measure twelve feet or six steps away, which gives the ratio of the width of the trench to its depth. You can expect a depth of eight to ten feet, as the deeper the trench, the more arduous it is to climb. The earth excavated from the trench provides the material one uses to construct the parapet. The earth, which has been thrown out of the ditch, gives shelter to the banquette; But the dirt which may be left over because of the strength of the ground, must be dispersed, or a rising of the earth at an oblique incline should be carried out before the edge of the trench, so that the enemy cannot see adequately into the trench. The trench must be faced diagonally on both sides and concealed in the direction of the enemy. The entrance, which must be laid on the opposite side, where the enemy comes from, is counted five steps, or eight to ten feet, which is marked with No. 4. These must be obstructed with trees placed in an abatis, together with their branches, behind which a number of fusiliers are set up, and such are defended by their branches. See here from Plan 1.

It is also possible, if the detachment is not strong, and the rampart is not beaten down by canons, to make the entrance as narrow as possible, and draw the ditch all around the hill, and we shall weave the coverings, which are passed over the ditch but this must be taken away at night or at the approach of the enemy; The enemy is thereby given even greater burdens, and the one who is to defend such a work must at all times see to it.

In this passage, I have spoken only of those who have an officer to direct them to raise field works at great speed, in order to assure themselves of safety in the event of attacks by the enemy. Should permanent works be erected, they generally employ engineers or officers who are assured that they have a knowledge the field-engineering.

Anyone who is an officer and wants to gain an understanding of this much-needed skill, should read *The Field Engineer*, published by the Saxon Mr. Thielke.[54] This is a very instructive and useful work for the officer who wants to gain an understanding of engineering in the field. He who follows my advice in this matter will soon be successful based on the knowledge he draws from that work. As for the defense of these works, that will be covered in the following section.

## Chapter 3

*On the Defense of Redoubts*

I have spoken frequently with many sensible officers about the defense of the field works, the greater part of whom would rather strengthen such a work than defend it. Therefore, it is well that their defense is so difficult, since we have seen some examples in the wretched war where soldiers, who were behind a weak field work have done wonders, and driven back the enemy, who has already jumped into the ditch.[55]

I have often spoken with many reasonable officers on narrowing defensive field-works. The greater part maintain that they would prefer to climb over the top of such a work as defend it. How is it possible, then, that by keeping the defenses as hard as we have seen and experienced in a few examples in the last war that soldiers who stood behind a weak work did wonders, and the enemy, who had already jumped into the ditch were resisted and beaten back?

Many of my comrades have seen Granby's men put up an epic defense in the hills, in the year 1761, when the battle of Vellingshausen was fought, under His Serene Highness, Duke Ferdinand of Brunswick and at the place where the Prince-elect, the Hereditary Prince of Brunswick commanded.[56] This hill was attacked with some courage by some French chasseurs. Some of them were thrown on the boards, which they had thrown over the ditch, to aid them in their ascent of the hill.

The defending unit was commanded by a Hanoverian major, a man who panicked at the moment of the attack. Their enemies carried it out with great liveliness.

The major then permitted the hill to be given over to the French. He let shame beat him and I did not miss him much; The commander-in-chief smashed the drums of the tambour, jumped in with his sword in his fist, and spoke to his men, who followed him, and repelled the enemies with the greatest courage.

The French commander, who attacked with his men so bravely, encountered misfortune, if I can call it so, on the edge of the moat.[57] His men were thrown back and taken prisoner, and put into a panic, where, after a few minutes, he gave up his soul with great bravery. He should have been lucky enough to be visited and deplored by the Hereditary Prince of Brunswick, at the last moment of his life. A good friend has assured me, who was an eyewitness to the event, that he was indeed lamented by this magnanimous and courageous prince. Happy is the little one who can finish his life in such a glorious place and sell his life so dearly to his prince!

We have not yet given an example that occurred the end of the last long campaign in the war. It happened on the hill at the Brücker mill.[58] From morning until late at night the French and Allied armies attacked each other under the fire of a number of heavy guns. The mill, which lay on the other side of the Ohm, and the hill, before which our men made only a petty and forgiving fire, were the key places of action. The hill was only held with a hundred men, who were replaced every half an hour. The exhortations to the regiments von Dittfurth and von Knyphausen were the most passionate. These units had to defend the hill by sending men in detachments. At that time, I was with the nearest regiment, and I myself was an eyewitness to this murder-hole. The barricade on the top of this hill behind which the brigade was to shelter was so shaved by the cannon fire, that when one was standing upright, he was not covered up to his knees. Because of this, the unfortunates who were sent in lost a fourth part of every detachment killed or wounded before being able to take any shelter. Still, the spot was defended with so much bravery that one did not dare to speak

French at the place where Ohm was flowing.

These examples show clearly enough the importance that lies in the defense of these works, do they not? And one can rightly quote the basic rule of Agesilaus.[59] This great king says that the strength of a city does not consist in the Moors, but in the bravery of the possession and in the cunning of the commander.[60] This principle, I say once again, can also be directed to the defense of the fortresses.

In my opinion, I think that the enemy, even if he was at the edge of the ditch, had still won nothing. Where do you place the bayonets on the rifles, if you want to stop the enemy by closing with him? It is a matter which the sole concern of a determined officer to encourage his men, and to try to get them out beforehand, that the battle would then begin, when the enemy leaped into the ditch, and climbed up the breastwork.

Would it therefore not be useful for an officer to be trusted to defend such a work, from which at night villagers with scythes, pitch-forks, and axes could be brought up, in order to send such forces against the enemy, in the event of the attack from them? One could put the people with these long weapons so that our men are deployed with guns between them. Thus, as soon as the enemy jumps into the ditch, it is no longer necessary to fire, but, with courage, turn to the bayonet, and attack him with the naked steel. How sadly the attack by the enemy would not fail, and how he would be thrown into confusion, as he had previously believed that he had won everything, yet as soon as he had jumped in the ditch he was suddenly deceived in his court. His courage would be undermined when he was attacked by such determined men, as he thought he had already surpassed all danger. This process will make him even more brittle, since the fencing with the naked steel have gone out of fashion.

Men will object to this, saying that the enemy will jump over the abatis and ditch if they made it up the hill. I hope, however, that it will be difficult to come so far. On the other hand, the enemy will feel the force of a storm, since he did not expect he would be so badly received.

Where is there not honor in such a courageous and brave defense? I am sure that a staunch defense against the enemy, though we may lose in the end, will crown us with laurels. Are we not, in such enlightened times, that one is more honorable when he puts up a stout defense than he who makes the attack? Does not the example which I have given at the beginning of this section show us the proof of it, and do we not find such magnanimous features of the heroes in the countenance of the ancients, when one was accustomed to practice cruelty to his prisoners? The history of Alexander the Great gives a convincing example of this. Such a gentleman as this great king, who proudly conquered by his agreement with the gods confessed when he received the Indian King Porus in his camp. The latter had made a brave defense but was now Alexander's prisoner. When Porus inquired as to his fate, Alexander magnanimously replied that he wished, if he were not Alexander, to be Porus. Thus, Alexander guaranteed the defeated king's protection.[61]

## Chapter 4

*On the Attack of the Field Works*

These posts are attacked either by force, in order to conquer them, or the enemy seek to seize them by cunning. This often happens when those who are to defend such places seek to live in safety which is the height of negligence. During the war, it was almost impossible to hear anything at all of surprises, since it was a science of vigilance and caution.

An officer, who is commanding in such a position cannot be vigilant enough, inasmuch as the peace and security of a whole army are based on his attentiveness. If he is deficient in this area, he will be remembered, both for the attacks he opens the army to, and the reproaches he suffers from his superiors.

It is seldom a matter of the day to day, without a good deal of money, to take a field work easily.[62] If this is provided, the more likely he is to achieve his purpose. Set up your artillery on the rising hill and let as fierce as possible fire upon it. It will be easy to make a breach in the walls, which can be used to capture the work. I will, however, make the case here, that an officer should take a fort half with force, and half by cunning, without the aid of bribery.

Before proceeding to the attack, one must try to find out the position and the layout of the entrenched post, either with his own eyes, which is best, or by spies, in order to develop a thoughtful plan of attack.

First, it is necessary to know all the approaches and paths leading to these posts, and how they are to be made. Second, one must know the strength of the crew who defend it. Thirdly, we must know how far the next post of the line, which may come to his aid, is separated from it. Fourthly, whether the fort we are attacking is provided with foxholes, palisades, and storms, and whether there are wolf-pits and chaff-mines in the same.[63]

If such a work endowed with defenses that adds something to its strength, then a certain number of his men, with axes, entrenching tools, hoes, and other implements, must be sent to make the wolf-pits. Before going to the place where the attack is to be done, one has to assign his men to their specific tasks, so that one does not have to repeat orders too many times.

The best time for an attack is one or two hours before daybreak, this is usually the time when even the most powerful must fight with sleep. It is necessary, however, to carry out the march in the greatest silence and discipline, and not to allow the men to smoke or chat, and to time your movement so as to arrive early enough at the place where the attack is to be undertaken. Everything depends on secrecy, speed, and proper timing, so that the enemy will not receive any news from our company.

If one encounters an enemy patrol, then one must lie on the earth, quietly, beside the path. If one perceives that he has not been seen by the path; it is necessary to leave the area quite calmly, which will make the enemy feel even more secure in his post. But if we cannot conceal ourselves from them, it is necessary to cut them off, and if possible, to do so without the slightest interference, and immediately attack the post. For if the enemy perceives that this patrol is not safe, he will surely be more on his guard.

If one can make several attacks simultaneously, it is best to do so; For the more attacks there are, the more confused the enemy is made. It is necessary, in particular, for the enemy to expect to have the least chance of quarter or to withdraw. If he sees that he is attacked on all sides, it will soon be the case. Those who are appointed only to make appearances must do so no more than according to agreed signs. These must make a fierce fire and haunt the enemy, so that they may draw the enemy's attention, while those who are the true assailants will leap into the ditch, blow the palisades and storm it with the axes and entrenching tools to make it easy to climb the breast-work

These attacks, however, must be directed to the tips of the angles, which are the weakest parts of the entrenchment. Those who lead the assault must hang the rifles over their shoulders so as to attack the enemy, as soon as they can ascend, with fixed bayonets.

While the latter part of the attacking forces are concerned with cutting the palisades, fascines, and overthrowing the breast-work, the other part, together with those of the forlorn hope, who must also endeavor to overcome the breast-work.[64] These men must fire fiercely on those who defend it in order to bring them from the main body of defenders to the work, along with those who are already in the ditch. We have enough examples of when illusions have turned into truths. I will here undertake a proposal which can be very controversial of a work, for I am sure that if a man is to be taken by force one day, he will be very upset.

It is necessary to furnish the men attacking with blinding shells, which must be loud as well as bright. Perhaps a few should be placed at first in the rampart, so that the enemy would be frightened by their attack.[65] But the fire-tubes of those who were blindly charged would have to be fired by a slow-burning match, so that the enemy would not notice it. These shells must be thrown into the works as soon as the edge of the ditch has been reached.

It is known that firing these shells behind the parapets, as long as they are covered by it, assures that the enemy cannot storm it until the shells have made their observations worthless. But as the attackers are not to be frightened of them, they still fear the enemy; It is possible to attack the hill at this time, and it will surely be too late for the enemy to notice the deception.

In the first siege of Kassel in 1761, under the firing of a number of heavy canons, I saw a hill taken with the greatest speed. This hill was on the left of the Dutch road behind the Mohnbach. It was occupied by a French captain with fifty grenadiers. One should not believe that people who made up a brigade which performed such a feat could be so forgotten.

The Count of Bückeburg, who commanded the siege, focused his fire upon the enemy's redoubt from a battery of heavy bombshells. Covered by the battery fire, a hundred Hanoverian grenadiers who were to attack the redoubt, and the reserve of the infantry regiment von Wutgenau, moved into position for their assault.

The French did not fall for the ruse of the artillery fire and suspected some fraud. They believed that the Count would drive them out by the fire. They did not realize the Hanoverians had moved forward until they had already ascended the redoubt. They paid for their impudence as barely a one of them escaped the resultant attack.

If the French had only looked at us at that time, when the fire of the cannons would not have obscured us. If they had only covered the place with a brigade, as the Hanoverians were already in the ditch of the redoubt, they would have received them with the bayonet on their rifles or with their long sabers. It would not be necessary for the Hanoverians to make such a good effort to take the redoubt. For an officer to show his authority, he must not allow a surprise attack which succeeds in gaining his position. He must in no way to be overthrown, in order to destroy all the attacks of the enemy.

Folard gives us the idea that the people who are to mount a fortified work should be armed with scythes and espontoons.[66] In my opinion I am very much in favor of these weapons. For what makes the enemy more stupefied, and what makes him more easily resolved than if he were attacked in an unusual and unexpected way? The great master of war leads us to an example, where he himself, by the aid of these weapons, ascended a hill, and to which he ascribes the fortunate outcome of his enterprise.

He said that when he had been given the command of Modena to assist him in the year 1706, he had proposed to the commander one morning in the beginning of the siege to take a work which the enemy had constructed the night before, which the sentries had failed to discover before dawn. He took the grenadier companies from the regiments of Brittany and Vexin, half of whom he had armed scythes and partisans.[67] The soldiers were armed in this manner in order to force out the enemy. This happened and Folard succeeded in his plan. The enemy lodgment was taken, and this kind of weapon (the partisan) gave the enemy so much horror that the men from all the posts which Folard's troops had taken on this side were driven out with terrible shrieks.

## Chapter Five

*On the Fortification of Castles, Churches, Manor Houses, and like Posts.*

The fortification and defense of castles and buildings deserves special attention. They often contribute a great deal to a successful attack by a large company, and the security of the army depends on them. There are examples where such a post, when well defended, has sometimes stopped the train of an entire army.

One finds an example of the preceding in the *Notes on Polybus of Folard*, where he describes the battle the Cassano, from which one can see how many people were killed by canister that had been shot from the French who defended the manor house at Adda.

Many don't know how bravely Chief de Battalion Lange of the Lieb Regiment defended the cemetery at Frankensberg with a hundred men against the whole Corps of Conflans, which was over two thousand men, and how many heads would be taken?[68] This cemetery would not have cost this corps casualties if Commander had not spared the place out of a feeling of patriotism.[69]

A general, though he is in the same position, cannot, in its defense, make up for the bravery of the officer who is the commander of the post. There is more amusement than experience if the general should try. An officer who has the plan that he can apply well here, and reduces the enemy during their advance, may, by such an opportunity, acquire an immortal glory, and make his fortune.

An officer, who is in such a post, must occupy the very first hollow, and before proceeding to the fortification, he must look around in the neighborhood, for which side the enemy will give him the most difficulty in order to put the strongest obstacles in the way. If the position which he is to defend is surrounded by a wall, and he possess enough people to occupy all the places, they must not be overthrown, and the church or the house should be looked upon as operated in the same way as the citadel of a fortress. One must be vigilante. It is always better for the enemy to find obstacles in his way.

It is necessary, however, to have a wall ten or twelve feet tall, and a trench which must be seven or eight feet deep. The latter, however, must be placed four or six feet from the wall, and the earth, in front of, shall be raised against the wall, so that it may be better suited to the height.

The gates and exits must be obstructed with manure, earth, or, better yet, with trees set fire and placed against them if the wall is high enough. Stones, however, must be kept in hand, in order to greet the attackers, who are always a great nuisance. The success of this was seen and experienced in the campaign of 1758, especially in the fighting near Ulrichstein, where the French colonel, Herr von Reid, was the commander of the men of Fischer's Corps.[70]

It is too much trouble to batter down the walls with shot; One must be satisfied with the fact that one can fire over the wall. For this purpose, scaffolding is placed behind the wall, for which one takes great tables, benches, drums, and benches, on which boards are laid. One must pay special attention to the wall where it juts out, as these are the weakest places; This is where the most troops should be posted. Care should be taken to reinforce and defend it by a heavy fire.

The place where the enemy is forced to retire, after having been forced to leave the wall, must be attacked first. Likewise, at the time of their retreat, a consistent fire should be made on the enemy. This is the point how-

ever, when everything I have proposed to obstruct their lanes of retreat must be made ready in order to obstruct their escape as quickly as possible.
But if one intends to make a stand at the position which was to be defended, it is also important to dig a trench around it. Then proceed as I mentioned above regarding how to put your men around the wall.

We must take care, however, to cut off all the trees and the hedges, so that when the enemy arrives, he is exposed from head to foot. Close all exits, as already mentioned, as well as the lowest windows. The staircase on the lower floor must not be forgotten either and to climb up, if a ladder is used, which, after being ascended, is drawn up behind.

Then men were put into the rooms, so that the enemy might find adversaries in every place. The defenders could fire out of the windows, and when they load, they place themselves against the walls, where they are sufficiently covered from small arms fire.

One should also place some men by the exits, in order to destroy those who wish to evacuate. Poles and kiln forks must also be on hand in order to repel the ladders, which the enemy will try to raise by hand to gain entrance.

One must be diligent in guarding all places, but especially at the house where roof corners must be opened, so that one can shoot at the enemy, and on his approach, one may throw stones upon his head. Here, as well as in all the rooms, there must be a lot of rocks, small beams, and stones laid by the hand, to greet the enemy in every place where he gets close. Especially one must not forget this in the rooms above the exits. For these places must be directed to his eyes. One must also break large holes over these, and station around them between two and four men. These additional men, as Herr von Folard says, must be given to a long pole, on which bayonets are placed; For here is a place where a thousand men can be compelled to fight to the death.

There should also be a great deal of fresh water close at hand, and a great deal of firewood to keep the fires going, where the water is continually boiling, and dump the water on the heads of enemies if they should try to climb the walls. I certainly believe that those who are received in such a way will be overwhelmed, and in turn run away.

If, however, there are several buildings in the vicinity of the post, which cannot be overcome by the weakness of the defenders, but, if the enemy is so strong that they might overwhelm the defenders, then, if time is left, it must be broken off, or if one is willing to spare the people, and at least let the animals of such buildings should be released, so that the enemy can not make use of them.

If one has done all that is described here as a prudent and courageous officer should, then the enemy will not be able to continue on his course. Instead, he is so weakened by such a courageous defense that he cannot have hope of a happy conclusion. One must not let his courage sink and seek to encourage others to be brave. For a brave soul will always find aid where the cowardly and the envious ones give up everything. The elevation of the soul, the thorough knowledge of the salvation, never shines more than in the most distressing calamities; These give us astonishing insights and resources which we might never have expected, and the waters are stronger than the necessity, as if our lives and salvation depend on them.

If, therefore, one has defended his post on the bravest night, and there is no way of hoping for any help. We must be as quiet as possible, then exit as carefully as can be done, gathering our people, forming a small column from the remnant of its detachment, which are as wide as the exit, and in this way, with the sword in hand, make our escape.

The enemy will not think it a courageous business, when he is humbled by such a hot day, and felt himself assured of his conquest of the post on the day. Likewise, where the night is also the mother of terror, by attacking then, you bring fear to your enemies beyond your strength.[71]

These means, which I have proposed, and which have already been carried out by many valiant officers, must be done in the greatest silence and order, against the desired target. It is unnecessary to shoot at a hostile guard; it is even better to refrain from such activity so that no noise is produced. Instead all is seized with the sword in hand.

This enterprise, when it is conducted with bravery and prudence, can never fail. For this reason, I will give an example of one of the greatest generals, who, for France, had been fighting like a Turenne and Conde. Mr. Folard provides such an example, and I will, in order that it may not lose any of its value, be obliged to give the example in his own words.

This great master of the war says: "The year 1705 gives me an example of a defense of a house, which is as bold as any one and just as worthy to be described. I heard of it on my passing through Prussia by an officer who had not the slightest advantage if he had told me anything on error. But because it is not my habit, that I write to the statement of one man, if I can inquire from others about the truth of the matter, I have given myself the permission to ask many persons about it. What I will say is the Count of Saxony, afterwards Marshal of France, who, with a great courage and much intelligence, a great diligence, and many not very common dexterities, combined with a great knowledge of all parts of war, by choosing one of the most learned and most skilled military men in Europe. He was attacked in a house at the time of the Diet in Poland. He was at Lemberg, where he was waiting for opportunity and a reason to go to Warsaw, where the court was then being held."[72]

“On hearing that a truce had been concluded between the Saxon troops and their enemies, he thought he had to take the opportunity to appear at court, and, towards the end of the January, he traveled with a great number of officers and his men. He came to a little town named Kraßnick. Here, he took his lodgings in an inn, the Cathetery, which is such a building, as the ones called by the Turks a caravansera. He could not continue any further, as there was a very heavy rainstorm, and the Poles had to pick him up in this place. Since the word spread that the Marshal was in that place, they sent off two hundred dragoons and six hundred cavalry led by M. Paschkonisti. Because they imagined that they would find the Marshal Count of Flemming, who came through that way there as well.[73] No sooner had he been at the table, the Marshal was told that many riders came into the village, and they were quickly approaching his position; If he were content to maintain his posts, he must quickly lay out his dispositions. It was impossible for him to defend all the sides and out-buildings of the house, which were distant from each other with only eighteen people. He placed his men two each in the sleeping chambers, with the order that if the enemy should appear, they were to shoot at those who would enter the lowest chambers. And as the Count was able to help his people through the stable, he set himself up with his remaining troops. He had only as much time as he needed to make his orders, for a moment afterwards the Poles attacked him. The doors were opened first. But as the ceiling was not very high, those who were on the upper floor, those who were below, held the rifles on their bodies without being seen, nor did they refuse to avail themselves of this advantage. The first, who entered, were killed on the spot. The others, who were astonished at this murder, saw that it would not be better for them to follow their comrades. Due to the marshal's deployments, his enemies imagined that there were more men down in the inn, though there was not a single man there, they left this attack to enter through the windows of the other rooms, which they had not seen, which allowed men to move from one room to the other. This made the Count of Saxony very embarrassed, who could not allow them to do so. Then he ordered his men together with the officers whom he had, to go out and attack them with the sword. The enemies did not think of such a bold enterprise and an unexpected attack, especially in the middle of the night, where courage outweighed numbers, and this is always held to be greater than it is."

"The Count had been wounded by a shot through doors, but his wound did not hinder him, and he fell upon the enemy, who had taken the first room. They were attacked, and almost all of them were killed or wounded. The others leaped out of the windows to escape. The Poles tried this approach with the same success, which forced the count's men to retreat. So, they were only able to cover the house, and they would wait for day to decide what they should do. The Count judged their intention well and had great cause to withdraw from their hands. Herr Pashkonisti, who was a junior officer of the House Guards, sent an order, and at the same time sent an officer to ask the Earl of Saxony to surrender, with the threat of burning him on the spot. He called to the officer that he should go back, but as one of his housekeepers heard he offered good surrender terms and went out to the window to surrender. To gain back control of the situation, he had to make a distasteful decision to have the Polish officer shot dead. The enemy was not deterred by this, but sent a Dominican Priest, who sought to see the Count a second time, but he was received like the officer.

"The Count, afterwards, gathered together all the men he had, and told them that no quarters could be hoped for either for him or for his men. He saw no means of assistance except if, with the sword in fist, they fought their way out and tried to break through; As the hostile troops were divided into various small parties, the main body of them was thus safe. The only thing that might happen to them would be that they would come upon one of the parties of their foes. The latter would fall effortlessly, and they would be able to approach with the sword in their fists without hesitation.

"This suggestion astonished some but was approved by others and generally accepted. So, fourteen men were sent out. At first, they observed a guard, which had nothing to do with the main purpose, and was therefore steered away from the house." How could it be imagined that a handful of men could make such a decision? It is, however, understandable, if we know what effect necessity and desires can have for one who wants to save his own life. They found the guard in such a state, as I have said, that they were taken down without a single shot being done. And these impassioned men went on to Gendomir, which the Saxons held.

Read this example with proper attention, and one will find how instructive it is for an officer. How quickly and skillfully his orders were given, and how brave so great a man. For he had already settled in for the night, when he made up his mind to attack those who had entered the room with their swords in their fists, and to drive them back. How quickly this great leader perceived that if he had not returned the officer and the Dominican, who had been sent by the Poles to summon him, he would be killed. To make the matter more unpleasant, few of his men would have been allowed to surrender. Finally, how wisely he had devised his and arranged his escape, to get out of the hands of the enemies, since all was by then lost.

Brunswick Troops in Canada
Light Infantry Battalion Barner
Jaeger, 1776.

# Chapter 6

*On the defense of Churches, Manner Houses and like Posts*

The planning and arrangement of the attack and taking of one these posts must be as thorough as that described above concerning the attack of field fortifications.

If such a post is filled with brave and determined men and is defended in the manner suggested in the preceding section, it will be difficult to take without burning the enemy out. But if one is determined and provided with burning coals, the more likely he is to achieve his purpose. Just place the flammables on the corners of the house, and stack the corners with them, or fill the object with glowing coals, so that it may be set on fire. So much the sooner will you put an end to your business. For once it begins to burn in such a post, the bravest ones will remember their salvation, and will yield themselves easily.

But if such aids are wanting, and one must take such a post, they must see that life is the least of what one has to sacrifice.

If one has come so near to the post that one can reach those who defend it with rifle fire; it is necessary to place the defenders under heavy fire, under whose cover one directs squad leaders at the corners, whereupon a number of courageous soldiers must rise to their windows or to the roof, in order to take the post in this way. If a number of them have achieved their objective, they must keep their men together, and seek to bring in the other from one room, and to fight with the sword in their fists, and to oppose them until the enemy has been so confined that he is compelled to surrender.

If this enterprise is not successful, and if the hostile commander of this post has made his arrangements as befitted a brave officer, and so arranged his men that he could not be affected in this way, then we must wait for the night and take refuge while keeping up a regular fire on the house.

To fire the house, take the bundles of fagots that have been dipped in tar, and look for them to be placed on the entrances, so that the enemy may be frightened by the smoke. They may even frighten him before they are set aflame. One can also take wet straw, which is infectious. This must be laid on the side where the wind comes from, which produces such a smoke that it will be hard to withstand.

But those who lay the fire must be covered from above, for their actions cannot be so concealed that the enemy would not be aware of them. The enemy can easily defend against such an attack, if he will only put a few stones on the heads of those to who are trying to light the fires.

We must, therefore, allow for the possibility of the attackers as well will be blinded by the smoke of the fires they set. The Lord de Ville proposes just such a case to us in his writings, and I am sure that this form of attack will be seen as crazy by some. Regrouping the men always takes time after the assault. It will be objected to me that before such an attack is made, the faggots should be made ready for carriage, as this author would suggest. Rarely has one been notified of the type of action described above long before it is ordered to begin. Ha! Seldom is there any time left between the command which is given, and the moment when one goes to attack. For one must always choose the shortest and most direct route.

I should think that the members of such a company would call on the local peasants, along with their ladders. I found an example of this sort of conduct in the remarks of the Lord Folard, of just such an action by the governor of King Gontram of Bergund, during the siege of Comminges, after which the former was condemned for his actions.[74] Folard mentions the use of carts to bring forth combustibles which, when set on fire, drove the enemy from their defenses.

In such a carriage, the top is covered with strong boards, so that the attacker cannot be effected and burnt from above. Those who are hidden under it are so covered from enemy fire, that the conductors of the load do not break, and one can double their number.

These firebrands are brought as close as possible to the house, from the fire of which the people who place them are safe enough. Two, three, or several pieces can be made from them, so that fire can be applied to the corners, to increase the fear of burning on the part of the defenders.

Could a petard be laid out of the arsenal, it would probably be the only and the shortest means of splitting the door, and of bringing the attackers into the place. The officer who attaches it can also approach the house by means of the help of the glare. I have examined a petard in the said arsenal, and find that in the absence of such, a large kitchen mortar can be used.[75] It can be loaded and fastened in the same way as in this case with a petard. The firing-hole, which is held at the top of the ground, the brackets with which they are fastened on the floor, and the hook with which it is attached can be given, when there is time to allow for these additions. But I cannot find the rehearsal and reinforcement of this proposed means, since I have made no attempt at it.

As a petard is loaded, as I understand the process, and as the Lord le Blond describes the process in his way.[76] This writer says: "You can force as much powder into the Petard as possible. Then, with thick double paper or felt, it is then covered with a wooden disc of the same size. This must be swept of the powder with a few blows but be sure that the powder does not lose its granular form. The remaining hollow section of the petard is filled with the wood, yellow wax, or Greek pitch, and it is covered. The gentleman de Ville assures us that their use is not old, and first invented in France."

We see, therefore, that for a brave officer concerned with the attack, as well as the defense of a post, must think and meditate on a thousand means of how he can thwart those who oppose him, and how a happy stroke can be obtained. But he must pay particular attention to the fact that he can save the soldier's blood, which is very precious. Nor must we undertake such things as seem to be impossible, and which taste much of madness rather than boldness. For one must be bold in war, but do not call the fearful intentions of exaggerated caution the advice of prudence.

A certain author says: "The intrepidity, which is connected with no moderation, has a side to me. It is only a grave contempt for death, a drunkenness of heart, which is only acted upon by the distraction, an agitation full of hatred, which blinds itself to the dangers, and presents itself completely contemptuously."

# Chapter 7

*On the Fortification and Defense of Villages*

My purpose was at first only to describe the actions which might be carried out by the small detachments of individual officers and the men under their command. But as I am certain that I do not have an officer who cannot afford, with the understandable pride, to reach the higher levels of his estate, I have included these concluding sections on the fortification and the attack of the villages and introduced a general concept of the behavior of detachments.

In this section of the treatise I will show the defense of the fortresses and houses how one should behave to counter the enemy with a stubborn defense in one of these posts. It will be seen from this that the security of the armies is based on the defense which is associated with the proper vigilance, insight, and determination. An officer in such a position is commander-in-chief, he understands his craft, and thereby attains the greatest fame.

The defense of villages and towns requires preparations, which are, as with the elements discussed in the former chapter, mostly remote. The only difference in this case is that these are more extensive, and consequently, require both greater effort and labor, as well as more people, for their defense.

The first concern, as soon as we enter a village, is to meet one the most distinguished of the inhabitants, whom we question about the characteristics of the region. We inquire about the terrain, any passes or outcroppings that may be suitable for planning ambushes. In addition, we inquire about the roads which lead to the enemy, as well as the enemy patrols, and how far away is the place where their first sentinels stand from us.

You now know all the different strategies, which have been known for many years. It is necessary to walk around the village, so that the size of the village can be truly appreciated, in order to be able to divide its people, block all the exits at the greatest speed, for which carriages are seized from which a wheel will be taken to improvise barricades with them. Branches are cut, the extremities of which must be removed to form abatis. The outermost houses of the village should be covered by these abatis, which are judged according to the proportion of branches on each. The branches are placed upon the hedges, where they create an illusion of greater depth.[77]

It is necessary, however, to inquire, on one's arrival, about the region which is leveled in the back and sides: whether there is a sunken path, gorge, or some other hidden place, whereby the enemy can secretly sneak in, is nearby Plan II, the ravine (h) is to be seen: such sloping angles must either be guarded, or they should be blocked with trees and deep trenches, so that the enemy could not possibly advance without the greatest difficulties. I once found myself in one of these wretched places in the preceding war.[78]

During the campaign of 1762, General von Gilsa, entered two villages through the Fulde, defended by the Saxons and attacked them in their posts, taking most of them prisoner. While this took place, Prince Ferdinand of Braunschweig had to slacken the assault on the Kraßenberg in front of Kassel, which the French had entrenched with great skill. I was with a detachment of thirty men sent to take a hostile earthwork on a hillside, which lay on the side of the village of Kirschditmold. The village of Walershausen, which was held by neither us nor by the enemy, was in at right hand. An old soldier of my detachment told me that a ravine stretched from the latter to the former village. I had the same information by six men, which was much to my delight. The Frenchmen came from Mehlheiden in the night and made an attempt to carry this way round; but they found men defending it and did not know how many of them there were, they drew back.

We must also look round, as soon as we have the requisites to defend ourselves, for a decent place which is behind us, and where we can retreat when we are overcome by a courageous counter-defense, or retreat before a superior enemy. As on the same plan the manor (g), which is situated on a hill, and where, for the safety of his retreat, an officer with forty men has been placed. This place must always be set up in advance so that the enemy does not prevent us from retreating.

These were, to a certain extent, the instructions which were to be implemented with the greatest speed, in order to secure themselves against the attack of the enemy. How, for example, a village is kept in a state where it is no longer necessary to live among the villagers as it has been abandoned; or in other cases where villages are used, as outposts, where a contingent is stationed for only one or at most a few days. But the defense of a village, which lies in the chain which covers the quarters of the army, upon which the peace and security is founded, must be organized by quite different instructions.

The man who is commanding in such a position has generally the order to defend himself to the last man. This may also be the case where a village is situated on the wing of an army, or where such a situation is so great that the enemy sees himself compelled to attack the army, or to take it out of the army. He can only be on the defensive and must maintain a certain position in which to cover a country, where many villages lie in the chain of its outposts, and where everything depends on the fortification and defense of such posts. In the cases which I have given here, one has enough time to put his post into the best defense. Here, too, one must not forget anything which can be done to strengthen their post, for it is always better to do too much rather than too little.

I added plan II here in order to further make my case.[79] The village (a) is one which has been condemned to such a defensive position and is defended by a detachment of four hundred men. The exits are blocked by carriages and trees (k), for which I have added traverses (B). By the time the enemy arrives, these are laid on a level where ditches (d), which connect with each other, have been dug, the space between which is obstructed by carts and trees (k), some of which are laid so as to be easily removed in order to deceive the enemy if one has done it properly. The churchyard (e), which is surrounded by a good wall, lies on a high point, and is sheltered in a good defensive position, covers the right side of the village. In the back, I have laid out two redoubts (c), which cover this area. On the left side are two large ditches (d), which defend this side of the village and the defense, which is fixed by great stones and trees, so that the enemy cannot possibly pass it.

The fortress has been laid out a little outside the village, for I do not hold with the opinion that if one is stubborn in the defense of the village, and that one includes themselves in the village, it is safe against the fires, which the enemy could easily start and drive us out. But if his fortress was laid out a little outside the village; it does not prevent us from our counter-attack.

If there is a court or church in such a village as this (c) which is convenient for defense; Then one must, as I have proposed in the fifth chapter, made proper arrangements, in order to make use of it in the case of necessity. We must, however, show the sign which serves to retreat, to those who lead the platoons, who must keep an eye out for it.[80] These must ensure that this is done in the greatest order, so that the enemy does not arrive at this place at the same time as we retreat, with the crew under whose shot this movement must take place.

It is not enough, however, that his post was properly entrenched, but we must also be vigilant in it, and we must watch out for its security. These must not be more than five hundred yards distant from one another during the night, and nothing more than fifty yards from the post. If there is a mountain near the station, one must be guarded on the same day, so that the enemy may be seen. This must be done on a church tower as well, which has the same end. One must also send out patrols, especially in the night, and even the commander of such a post must occasionally visit the posts at uncertain times.

It is in the summer that one stands in such a post; The soldiers must build their own huts for shelter, so that no one has to go into a house. The men must also be allowed to take only what is necessary, so that there was no waste. But if it is in winter, and the weather is so severe that it is not always possible to stay in the huts, the people who are not in service can be quartered in the day; but they must always be counted at night. They must be kept together in those houses, which are nearest to the fortress, and which are called noise-houses, so that everyone may be on his appointed post.

But if the village should be so spread out that the whole extent cannot be covered because of lack of manpower, then it is necessary to choose the part which is most favorable to the defense, and to cut it off from the others, and to occupy it as well as possible. If, however, we find houses which lie outside of our entrenchment, and which give us a view of the enemy, who cannot help his assault, and cannot be changed in any way, these must be burned. But we must not go at once to this terrible extreme, which will produce too many unhappy men, but rather not doing so as the approach of the enemy, for which the necessary things are made ready to be put into the action every moment.

## Chapter 8

*On the Attack of Villages*

Since the fortification and defense of villages requires many of the same insights as that of the small post, it is precisely in the attack on those places which many of the hardships and obstacles that cannot be foreseen or avoided lie.

One must be fully and precisely instructed as to the defenses and numbers of troops both before and without such a post lest he be attacked by the strength of the enemy. He must be aware of the entrenchments, of the ways in which the enemy may try to lead us to him, such as would be antagonistic to obstacles, and all factors on which the defenders' hopes are based. According to all these reports, from the landlords and the scouts, who are found for money in all places, one must design his plan, and carry out the enterprise with due intelligence, courage, and determination.

It is wretched when the man who commands in such a posture places too much reliance on his fortifications, and therefore rejects the necessary and proper vigilance. If this is so, one has won the game by being able to attain to their purpose by cunning. But if the villages is guarded with the proper vigilance, the attack requires as much violence as cunning, and one can achieve this by the aid of the night.

For example, if a hostile village is attacked by five or six hundred men, half attacked by cunning, half by force by a detachment of five hundred men. Plan III will explain the matter even more.[81]

As to the instructions and prudence that must be applied to the march, I refer the reader to the first chapter, where I have dealt with them, for these are the same for the great as well as the small detachment. It is understood from the very same that the enterprise must be kept secret as much as possible, so that a soldier or a resident of the place where they are marching out of could learn of it. Otherwise the whole thing might easily be discovered by a hostile clerk or transgressor. It is, therefore, a good thing that, a few hours beforehand, the place should be sent out that no one can leave the places occupied by your troops, so that if a hostile spy is in your midst, he must remain in it.

If a commander is so close to enemy positions that he is only a few hours away from it, and can march on it and arrive early in the day, then it must be so arranged that he made his approach one or two hours before daylight to the place from which the attack should be made, for this is the shepherd's hour of invasions.[82] One has to choose a place like this carefully, a place where he can keep hidden, in case he arrives too early.

In Plan III, the village (a) is that which is so assaulted by enemies: (b) is the hill, which is a good quarter of an hour from the enemy, behind which one is hiding long enough to prepare and be ready to attack. We must have a signpost which guides us as far as possible to this place. One must also have the proper kind of troops to make these attacks, which must be carried out and at all times commanded by ten proficient officers.
If one arrived at such a place without the slightest hindrance, his force must make their attack as quickly as possible, according to the plan already made.

The detachment is five hundred strong, two forces (d, e) each of a hundred and twenty men, are appointed to carry out the actual attacks, and two additional units (f, g) of eighty men are held in reserve.

The commander-in-chief 's house is besieged by an officer with forty men, who must attack with force, jump over the bridge and at once bombard the house, so that the enemy might be cut off. But he must also have a vigilant eye on the enemy, in case they should launch a counter-attack. The officer should, therefore, send out patrols momentarily after making his attack. Should he be attacked, he cannot retreat in disorder or he will sacrifice everything as he leaves the ramparts. An officer who, in this case, defends such a post, must also lay a quantity of firewood or trees upon the bridge. Then, if he himself is overwhelmed and must retreat from the enemy, he can, by this means, prevent the enemy from advancing.

Those who lead such attacks most frequently march to their positions, while the others, who have to wait for them to get in position, must wait for them until they have received the signal which is the sound of shooting. The enemy who are left guarding the weakest intervals, which are only defended by people who are placed on the wagons or hedges, so that the attackers will turn the attention to them. In other places, where the defender depends on the strength of his entrenchment, are where he is least likely to suspect the attack. A hundred men were retained as a reserve (h,), with which the town, where the multiplicity of force is employed by the enemy, can come to its aid.

All the units must have an officer with twenty men at the front, who undertakes the beginning of the attack with the greatest vivacity, and which the rest of the team follows some fifty steps to the rear. The men in advance sneak up as near as possible, and with those supporting, double their steps, and seek with them at the same time the enemy entrenchment. The small units, which are supposed to march at the head, must be six men deep and as closed as possible, so that the attack has the proper strength and force.

As soon as they are close enough to the enemy that they can fire with the proper effect, they give a salvo and advance with fixed bayonets to set up the entrenchment. For the more courageously the enemy is attacked, the more horror is caused to him, and the sooner we achieve our goal. There must also be a few pioneers in a small detachment marching on the flanks, so as to take the walls, which are perhaps a part of the line of entrenchment, and are defended by the enemy, and throw other obstacles along the way can clear

Those who take part in the shock attack must make a deafening fire, which they may associate with a great horror: but these too, as much as possible, must hold back once they have achieved their goal of discomforting the enemy. For how many examples are known, where the fake shocks have turned into the true ones.

As soon as the troops are assembled in one place, commanders of the same will have to detach them to the right and left. Regardless of the weight against them, they must courageously drive the enemy together in one place. Everyone who leads one of these troops must tell his people that no one will leave his unit and plunder. For, as many examples are known, the best of such attacks have been defeated by such disorder, and such crimes cannot be too severely punished.

Those who are made prisoners must be enclosed at the entrance of the village in the nearest houses, and the guards will be drawn up with fixed bayonets. The guards are made up of men from the reserve and placed at the entrances to the above houses.

If the place is attacked with bombs, we must not for a long time be concerned with the attack on the same. But they that attack courageously with the bayonet has the best chance of success. If one can do this, it is best. For a courageous attack, as I have already said more than once, the bayonet is the best means of bringing the enemy to surrender. An example of which the Battle of Minden, which was won by the duke of Ferdinand over the French in 1759, is entirely convincing.

On the day of the battle, Herr Generallieutenant von Dittfurth, who was the colonel of the second battalion of guards, came upon a French battery of twelve canons, which was supported by a regiment of grenadiers. Without wasting a moment, he moved into position and at once threw himself upon the enemy with his battalion, with bayonets fixed, and captured the pieces, and made the most part of the covering party prisoners.

If the enemy has taken up a position within a village, entrenched himself, and selected a place for his refuge, one must direct his attack on this place. All those who lead troops must, according to their position, concentrate their forces and attack the strong point courageously and bravely, as if they are berserk.[83] If one finds houses in this area, which appear to be a nuisance to the attack, they must at once be taken, and the enemy fired at. If, however, the place where the enemy is going to go, and where he will try his utmost, is a court or church, which he has set up with great dexterity, then it must be sought in this way: after having been asked for a capitulation, when the means of attack had been proposed to the attack of these posts. If one is supported with canons, or has taken away the enemy's, the first thing to do is to bombard the place until it catches on fire.

Then, according to the order which one has from his chiefs, the defenders must either correct and defend the entrenchment of their position, or completely destroy all that is useful, and retreat. But if, on account of the brave defense of the enemy, the attacker was not able to take the post, it is necessary to consult reason, and to avoid pointless losses. Before attacking then, it is necessary to set up lines of retreat, and to arrange them as I have proposed in the ninth chapter, which deals with the retreats, to which I refer the reader's reference.

Jaegers in the field, 1770's

# Chapter 9

*On Retreats*

It is impossible that all the cases which may be encountered by an officer in the field can be cited; we must be satisfied with the fact that we accept only certain things as a whole.

As in the case of the house, there are examples of an officer who must have been entirely forgotten by the retreat of a corps through the order of a commander, or abandoned him in his post, and has thus had to withdraw in the face of the enemy. If an officer, on his march, despises the foundations and rules which I have referred to in the first section, it is possible that an unexpected attack by the enemy who pursues him, might surprise him. The officer should be made aware of it early on, in order to make a proper constitution. If he sees himself forced to retreat by a strong party of hostile infantry, he has in his feet the power to do so. If, however, he were to encounter a man who was superior to him in speed, it would not be possible for him to pass through obstacles, or for a post, for example, a house, mill, or chapel before the attacks. He must then form a column out of the men under him. This may be as small as is necessary; still, for them it is always best to retreat. It sends itself to all the districts, and in this case, they can be fired on all sides.

In the case of mounted troops, it will be difficult for the bravest rider, if the troop remains in order, to pass through such a dense body; For the troop must throw several men into the house, as in a square, where only one man stands up.[84] We must, however, always remain as close as possible to the closing-up of the hussars and other cavalry. If they come near, one makes a halt and on all sides and in front, leaves the first rank on the side where the enemy makes an attack, fires, and shows them the point of the bayonets. But one must never fire in vain, and always seek to continue his march.

If some friendly troops should come too close to each other and fire upon one another; After this happens a few times, they will no longer hit too hard, but be more careful. For the cavalry, especially the Hussars, are not easy to make prisoners by a handful of foot soldiers or jägers, unless they shoot their horses to death. This is especially the case with the French cavalry, of whom there is no great cause for fear. Not for the sake of their heartiness, for this people give nothing to anyone else; but in this case the loss of the horses to the commander of the squadron is sufficient is their responsibility. The hussars try to make the infantry disorganized by swarming, scolding, and shooting, and to take supplies from them.

If they see that their detachment is in order, the noise, the shooting, which is never of worth, does not bend, and tries to punish the most daring; soon they stand down from their enterprise. I know that a subordinate officer of the Fusilier Regiment von Knyphausen, who on the day when the first siege of Kassel was lifted in 1761, stood on the Moncheberg on command, and from his boldness with his men the enemy position was approached on his retreat. When he was ordered to fall back, he was followed by more than forty volunteers and Hussars for a good quarter of an hour, and they could not do anything to him, as he remained with his detachment, though the commander of the enemy Hussars came so close that he wounded the sub-officer with a saber in his chest.

But if such a detachment is ninety to a hundred men, one could make a column of seventy-four or eighty-eight men, who had six or seven men on the front and twelve in the side. Those still remaining from the detachment could be divided into four small troops, which now defend the column, and fiercely fire upon the riders, who are attacking. But you must also order that they do not shoot unnecessarily, and you must take the most courageous. If these are driven back by the invading enemy, they are the flanquits [flankers] of the column;[85] It is necessary, therefore, to indicate to each of them the place where they are to fight.

But if such a detachment were the strength of a battalion of four or five hundred men, it would be a closed battalion, which is the advance guard of an army, or, in another case, must retreat before a superior enemy; It cannot be in a better formation than I have just proposed. In this case the column can emphasize the strength of such a detachment.

If this is the case, then his battalion or detachment is divided into eight platoons.[86] The first holds front, five others sit with their right behind the first, and back as hard and closed as possible. The seventh and eighth pelotons, which are still left, are divided into four equal units, of which the two flanks of the head meet the two of the tail.[87] These also should be sent to fire upon an approaching enemy.[88]

However, in such cases, one must be very careful not to dwell on his march. For the hussars or cavalry would like to lead in the advanced units, so long as their infantry came along to support them, and only delay our march by their stretching. We must, therefore, consider all cases which may arise in this state.

The second example, which I have found in the remarks of the Lord of Folard, shows us that the column, in times of retreat, is the best movement, by which a detachment infantry might easily withdraw from a superior force of cavalry. The first occurred in the year 1476, when thirteen thousand Spahi invaded Friuli. These very brave riders, however, were not capable of throwing over a unit of the Venetians, led by the captain Montone. The latter retreated in a column, and that was the reason that the enemies could not harm him.

The second example is from the war which Charles the Twelfth had brought against King August of Poland.[89] The General von Schulemburg (the author of this article), the greatest expert on the infantry of his time, drew back with four or five thousand foot-soldiers in the Polish Plain, and more than eight thousand cavalry, who were led Charles the Twelfth himself. The infantry fought in column, whereupon the Swedes were stymied. The Swedes pursued them as far as a stream, where a mill stream lay, which the General von Schulemburg had taken, whose course favored the Saxons in their retreat.

Though these, like many others of this kind, show that one can choose nothing better than the column for retreat. The square does not give way easily, and for this reason, is the only maneuver, whereby the infantry can withdraw from a superior cavalry. I will also give an example from wartime of the advantage of this formation. We must, however, bring this matter into motion, if we are assured in the first place, that we are not incorrect in our understanding of the terrain which we must pass. For all the movements of the infantry that are made near brave cavalry, when the leader of the cavalry understands his craft, and is able to draw inspiration from the slightest disorder of his opponent, seldom strike well. It is, therefore, to say that this movement is best only when one marches in a great plain; Which is also demonstrated in the example, which I shall cite here.

At that time, the colonel, Herr von Sclotheim, commander of the first local Grenadier battalion, which consisted of the four companies of the Guards, drew more than twenty French squadrons from Charles to the bridge over the Edder von Möllerich in a period of three hours, in the greatest order, and as a man who knew the strength of the foot-soldier perfectly. The enemy cavalry attempted to cut down on this formation, but they foresaw that if they were to be brought to their purpose by the power and quantity of their cavalry, they would cost them a great number of valiant men, and that the grenadiers were under the command of a brave fellow-soldier, and their lives would be sold dear enough. So, the Duke of Broglie, who was at the head of the enemy cavalry, ordered these brave men to be drawn, and admired their retreat as a connoisseur of the war; Where he still added these words to one of his adjutants: "Respect these brave Grenadiers."

## Chapter 10

*Of the Actions of the Small Parties of Infantry*

It was in the last war between the French and allies almost expected that an officer with a small party of infantry would perform brilliant tricks since the countries wherein this war was fought were every low and perfectly situated for company-sized actions. We know that Westphalia, Hesse, and also Wetterau are so intersected with forests and mountains, that an officer with thirty to forty infantrymen, without risking much, can resist the enemy a long time. One finds few large plains in these countries, and on the other hand there are large areas where it is easy to hide a troop of infantry.

I do not know why you would want to give the hussars or mounted light troops alone the preference in this type of warfare. There are numerous examples where an officer with thirty mounted troops, who understood that part of the war, having done marvels to inflict the greatest damage on the enemy; and before he was caught again, he had deceived the enemy in a hundred ways.

Should it not be possible, then, for such tricks could be carried through in such intersected (broken) areas by units of the infantry of the same strength? On the other hand, I will object to the assertion that horses, without much difficulty, and much more quickly, will be able to make a wide march, and that they can retreat more quickly from a superior enemy; But did not the infantry have much to advance as well? At the same time, it is not necessary to provide the latter with forage, which is already a principal object of such movements. For all of these reasons, despite the objections, infantry could perform best in this type of fighting. Man can also hide much more comfortably and easily on foot than on horseback and can approach a hostile post more easily and with less noise.

Only an officer who practices certain martial traits will take pleasure in this part of the war. These include: that he knows the country in which he will go and knows how to conceal from all parts of the world the fact that he is hiding during the day, and that he marches very cautiously at night. He avoids the great plains as much as possible, and at all times the most developed and most congested districts during his stay.

In this case, however, it is not easy to decide what sort of soldiers are to be chosen for these detachments. They must be healthy and well-guarded, and the commander must be assured of their loyalty, and that they will not run away.

It is thus seen that an officer who directs such a party must be at his peak. He must, as I have said, know precisely the regions of the country in which he is going to operate. He must, therefore, inquire as to the best of these lands, to inquire among the landlords by kindness and reward for the principal supplies which he may be able to devour on his way, and, according to their statement, all the odd strange places. For example, he must be aware of the bridges, landmarks, glades, overgrown areas, forests, and the like, so that he can set up his advance beforehand. Finally, before he takes a step forward, he must think about how he will return, for he has to know more than one route in case one is blocked by the enemy.

I have already mentioned that one must only march at night: this is a chief rule for such a party, which must take refuge only in the cunning. Especially when one is near the enemy, one does not have to be seen in the day, so as not to be betrayed by those who live in the country. Mainly when one is in enemy territory, one cannot be concerned enough with such treachery.

If one is compelled to look for food for the troops, then one must approach a place at night. If it is situated in enemy territory, then you have to spend some time searching for a friend. It would be a good thing to bring some guides with you, just as people's language would be well known. These must be sent with a sub-officer to the village from which the food is to be taken; They must sneak in without the slightest noise, knock at the first house as fast as possible, and inquire of the inhabitants, so that they cannot be equally wise, according to friendly and hostile parties. If they take the account of the inhabitants, that they are sure of their loyalty, they must be led to the local chiefs of the place, and they must inquire afterwards, after the sought-after food. The subordinate officer demanded enough food for from one to four hundred men, from which he has left the inhabitants enough for a hundred men. He does this in order to win them over by not taking everything. If the detachment is thirty strong, he shall have the necessary maintenance for three or four days.

The subordinate officer loads his supplies on a wagon, and takes it about two hundred paces from troops, where he holds this, and he places a man on watch, and announces his arrival to the leader of the party. Then another officer orders a few men to the wagon and allows the food to be carried by them to the troops.

If we land in enemy territory, we must seek in the same manner the chief inhabitants, who are to the commanding general of the army great irritants. But one must at all times deal with the people of the country in a humane way and do not cause them the slightest injury. Because if they become friends, so are you mostly happy in their country, and besides, what woes can a resentful people wreak on your weary troops during the night?

If one is on the march, one must always, as I have already indicated in the first section, move fifty steps forward, and also as far from his troops on the sides, whether they hear of something or not. During the days on which they are forced to march, these men must look diligently, and all that they discover must be reported to the leader without loss of time, in order to evade all hostile parties.

If one encounters a hostile party in the night, one gets near the road and goes to ground, and is as quiet as possible, for one is perceived the least as soon as the closer one is to the earth. If the party's strength is not known, or it is a different catch, or is it that of the hostile army; Then they must be allowed to rest. But if one is informed of a hostile party by the inhabitants, which is equal in strength to their own; It is necessary to hide in a ditch or behind a hedge, on the side of the road, which must fit, and then, as soon as they are next to us, attack with the sword in his fist. For by the shooting we make noises, it does not help the night, and, notwithstanding all our good preparations, there could still be another detachment in the vicinity which could intervene and undo all we hope to accomplish.

One must also be careful not to be seen again in one place, especially near the enemy army. For here the joy would not last long, and one was in danger of being captured quickly.

The best place for creating inconveniences for an enemy is when one is on a common line between two hostile armies, or between the hostile army and one of its constituents. Here is a place where one can carry out the deeper pranks, if one does not fail to act with the proper prudence. In such a place one can collect generals, their equipages, and baggage, and couriers, which go back to the army. A good catch has been made. Then we shall return to the army by way of the road, and we shall return in good fortune.

I will here, for example, quote the positions which the allies and the French army assumed in the war.[90] The first was at the Diemelstrohm, which was in the neighborhood of Kassel. I do not know what an officer with thirty or forty men on foot, in this case which I have here, would be in the way to go to Streiserenen to Geissen, Frankfurt and Hannau? I certainly believe, though one must occasionally have to overcome difficulties in a house, that his efforts would be easily paid for.

It might be objected how the rivers, which are often used in this way, are to be approached, that cavalry is much easier to put to work in these areas. I cannot, however, allow this objection to a great extent, since the crossings of the rivers are so often seized that one can come across with men rather than with horses. Secondly, where is there a river where there are no barges by which one can cross the greatest rivers? I know around Kassel in a distance of four hours, ten places where one can get over the Fulde in this manner without counting the guides and bridges.

In these cases, however, we must make a display, and carry out such tricks by the aid of the night, for the night is an aid which makes things possible for us.

Thus, before going over a river with their troops, one must send over some men who are to patrol a half an hour into the country in the new manner, which I have set out. The men are to inquire after the enemy, so that one cannot, without inflicting casualties, be pushed upon by an enemy party after his passage.

The Lord of Cointe gives me an example of a Dutch partisan in his remarks on the retreat of the ten-thousand Greeks. This is very instructive, and one can see from this that, in the case of what I said and say of this matter, it could not be any clearer how one should behave in such cases:

"This partisan called himself Guetta and served against France in the War of the Spanish Succession, which was caused by the death of the Spanish King Charles II. It was in the year 1707, when this officer of Ath, a citizen in the grassland of Hainaut undertook his mission. He divided his force, which was thirty strong, into equal parts, and went as far as the heart of France. He showed them the place where they were to meet again. A party he positioned in the wood of Chantilly, which is nine French miles from Paris; and he took the second to St Quentin, near St. Denis, and he kept the point where he was between Paris and Versailles. The soldiers whom he retained were disguised, and entered various inns, which are situated on the great road between these westerly places. On one of these, the Merz, he saw the Duke of Orleans going forward, but it was the middle of the day, and nothing could be done. Two days after, he saw the Dauphin and the Royal Princes, who had too great an accompaniment to try any enterprises on them.

The Customs Commissioner, who had crossed the Seine at the bridge, had seen this man's way about it, and he also saw it for the present. He was stopped by an obstruction of a falling tree, which is at the bridge. To his misfortune he was the one to whom this area was most well-known. On the same evening, when the leader had been gathered with his men, he saw a carriage on the street, which he approached, and saw that the servants who stood up behind bore the king's livery. He held the pioneer, who had the torch in his hand, and ordered it to be extinguished. Thereupon he approached the carriage, and showed the minister, who was in it, that he was a prisoner by the king's order. The officer asked him with the utmost courtesy to get out of the car and place his hands on a horse. A servant from this gentleman asked the officer to be allowed to follow him to his master, but as he threatened to kill the servant, if he fancied this, he yielded himself willingly.

The leader and his nine men made their way through the wood of Boulogne to St. Quentin, where he found the second part of the detachment, which at his command always had to keep a postman ready, since they had lost their signpost. They lost their way along this path, and many hours passed by until they reached the place. At this time, the servants of the minister, whom they had all had to carry with them, had told and retold the story of their master, which caused a great stir. They sent to all the commanders of the frontiers, in the greatest urgency, with the command that they should, at the greatest speed, overthrow all those trying to go out into the country. The king himself sent for a detachment from the Garde du Corps to the partisan.

It is easy to see, therefore, that the officer did not march on this voyage, and that for a minister, who was accustomed to every comfort, was very troublesome. The latter was very sorry for the others, and he ordered the minister to rest for the hour, as leisurely as he could. The couriers had handed over their orders at such a speed, that the partisan, when he was still in the wood of Chantilly, already heard the alarm bells ring. He was very doubtful of the success of his enterprise. But he was fortunate enough to reach the city of Hamm in the province of Picardy, which is thirty miles from Paris. When he had scarcely passed this city, a hostile detachment of cavalry, under the Marquis of Livri, made him a prisoner. The Herr von Beringen, the Minister, whom the Mayor had always met with very politely, asked the Marquis not to inflict the least harm on this officer and his men, and compelled him to dine with him in the evening. It was in Paris, where the wife of this minister gave the partisans a very handsome gift, when she heard the human and very courteous behavior towards her husband."

It is, therefore, seen by this very instructive, just, and strange example, when one takes the character of the province of Isle de France, as one has to cast out his people, when one has chosen a place for such a company, and how to behave in such a manner.

Look at the character, and remember that the partisans had thirty men, whom he saw in the wood of Chantilly, which is four German miles from St. Quentin, wherever he places ten men. This place was not a German mile from the bridge over the Seine, in whose territory he was with the third part of his detachment. These soldiers, whom the officer kept, were certainly disguised, for it would otherwise have been impossible for such people to be allowed to frolic around like this. They left the day unhindered to look happy, but at night they gathered with their leader to carry out the raid.

I also believe that this man would not be defeated if he had not been caught by someone who knew this region. It is seen that, as I mentioned in the beginning of this section, people, who know the country in which they wish to go, must be carried with them, but there was also a fault in the fact that this enterprise, so wisely conceived, failed the partisan, who did not carry with him the servants of the minister. If he had done so, he would certainly have gotten away with his enterprise.

In spite of all this, this very rare example should not be rebuked, because of its unhappy end for the partisan. Likewise, he should, by no means be blamed, but admired, and his example brought to our late descendants. All I want to say is that an officer cannot be too careful about such an enterprise.

Printed

To Kassel in the orphanage = letterpress Teren

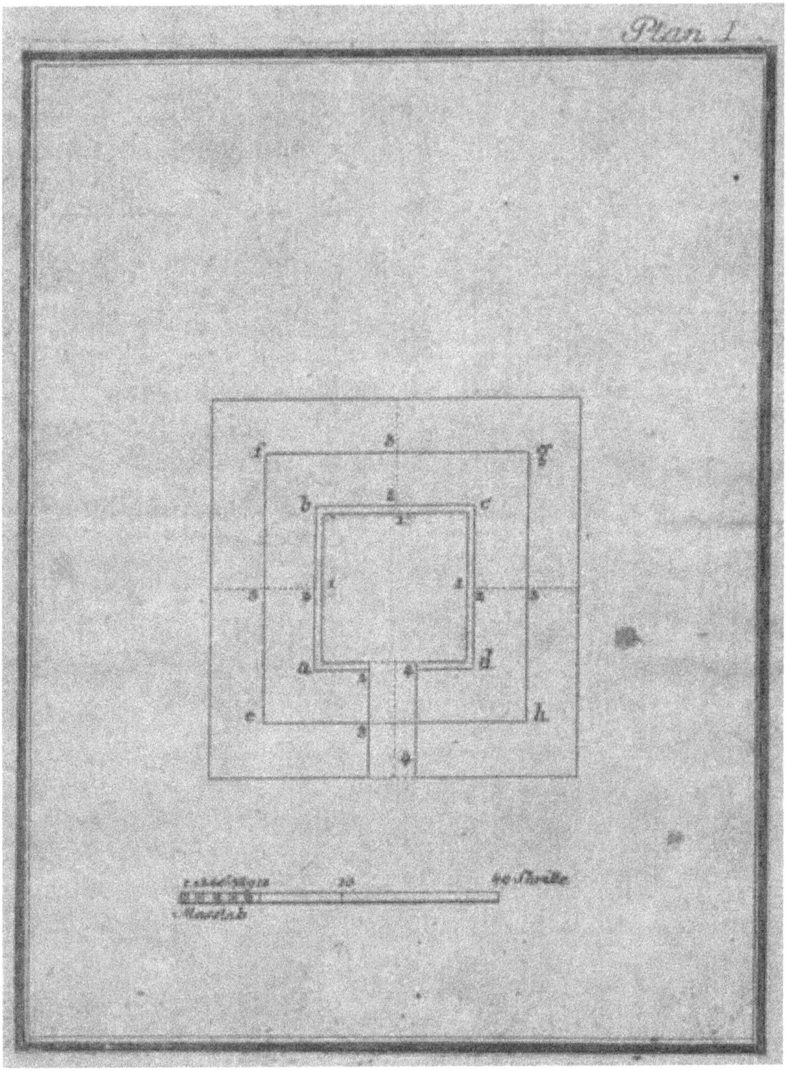


Plan 1

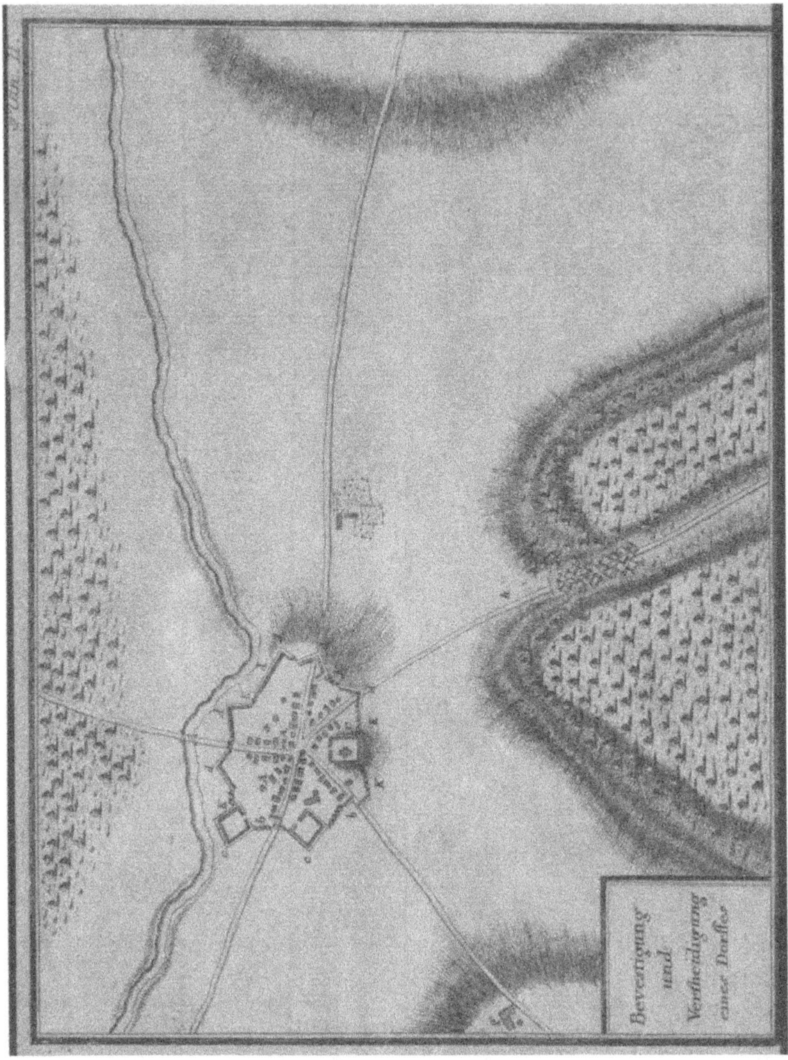


Plan 2

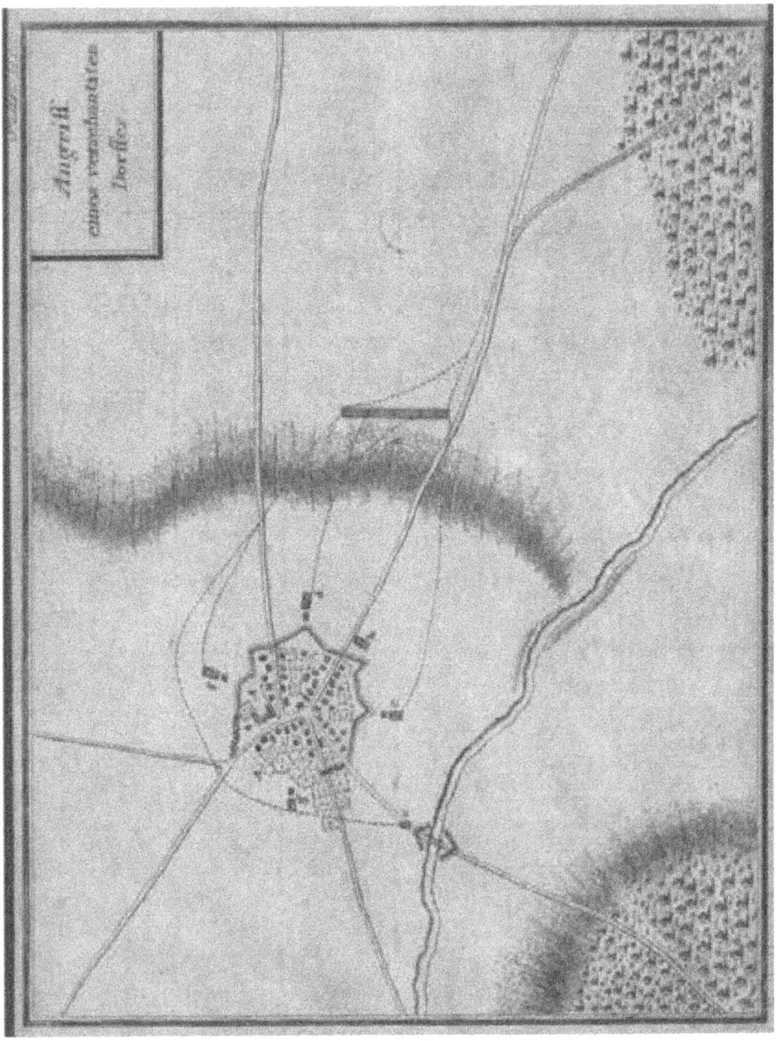


Plan 3

# Endnotes

[1]Hereinafter given as *Thoughts* or *Gedanken*. On the military enlightenment, see Azar Gat, *The Origins of Military Thought: From the Enlightenment to Clausewitz*. Oxford: Clarendon Press, 1989. For a much more timely and wide-ranging discussion, see Christy Pichichero, *The Military Enlightenment: War and Culture in the French empire from Louis XIV to Napoleon*. Ithaca: Cornell University Press, 2017.

[2]M. de Jeney, *The Partisan: Or the Art of Making War in Detachments* (English edition, 1760).

[3]On the re-emergence of light troops in eighteenth century warfare, see James R. Mc Intyre, *The Development of the British Light Infantry, Continental and North American Influences, 1740-1765*. Point Pleasant, NJ: Winged Hussar Publishing, 2015. For a very useful discussion of their use in the seventeenth century, see George Satterfield, *Princes, Posts, and Partisans the Army of Louis XIV and Partisan Warfare in the Netherlands (1673-1678)*. Leiden: Brill, 2003.

[4]For basic biographical information on Ewald, see, Tustin, *Ewald, Diary of the American War a Hessian Journal*, New Haven, CT Yale University Press, 1979, p. xxiv.

[5]Tustin, Diary, xxv. See also Carl von Ewald, Ewalds Levnetsløb. p. 2

[6]Mark Henry, "The Hessian Army of the Seven Years' War." in *Seven Years War Association Journal*. 8.3, (Spring 1994) p. 41.

[7]Carl von Ewald, *Ewalds Levnetsløb*, p. 2.

[8]Johan Ewald, *Diary*, p. xxv.

[9]Unless otherwise noted, the preceding derives from Rudolf Witzel *Hessen-Kassels Regimenter in der Alliierten Armee 1762*. N.P.: Norderstedt Books on Demand GmbH, 2008.

[10]Carl von Ewald *Johannes Ewald: Bilder aus dem Leben eines Soldaten*. Staatarchiv Kassel, Best. C19 Nr. 7217.

[11]Duffy, *Military Experience in the Age of Reason*, pp. 73-74.

[12]Ewald, Ewalds Levnetsløb,p. 2.

[13]These sources include the introductory not in Ewald's *Diary of the American War*, Tustin, ed. xxiv-xxvi. This is clearly based on the bi-

ography of Ewald by his son, Carl. Additional information on the elder Ewald's services in the Seven Years War were gleaned from Carl von Ewald *Generallieutenant Johann von Ewalds Levnetsløb.Copenhagen*: Riises Boglade, 1838, pp. 2-6. Finally, an anonymous pamphlet in the Hessian Archives attributed to Ewald but more like the work of his son as it describes the death of Johan von Ewald in some detail provided some additional information. See Carl von Ewald *Johannes Ewald: Bilder aus dem Leben eines Soldaten.* Staatarchiv Kassel, Best. C19 Nr. 7217.

[14]Ewald *Ewalds Levnetsløb*, p. 2.

[15]On the details of Ewald's uniform, see Pengel, *German States in the Seven Years' War.*

[16]Ewald *Ewalds Levnetsløb*, p. 2.

[17]Ibid, 2-3.

[18]Ibid

[19]Ibid.

[20]Ibid, 3.

[21]On the count von Schaumburg-Lippe, see James R. Mc Intyre, "Scion of the Enlightenment: Field Marshal Friedrich Wilhelm Ernst Graf zu Schaumburg-Lippe-Bückeburg." *Journal of the Seven Years War Association.* 21, 3 (Spring 2018):24-63

[22]Ewald, *Bilder*, p. 2.

[23]Anonymous "Militär in alten Mauern" September 13-14, 2003 Internet. https://web.archive.org/web/20031005141352/http://www.hessenmilitaer.de/amoeneburg.htm Last accessed September 28, 2016. See also, Carl Renouard *Geschichte des Krieges in Hannover, Hessen und Westfalen von 1757 bis 1763.* 3 Bände, Cassel, 1863-64 , pp. 784-796

[24]Ibid.

[25]Ibid.

[26] Ewald, *Picture*, p. 2

[27]Ewald, *Gedanken*, pp. 15-16.

[28]Ibid.

[29]Militär in alten Mauern

[30]Ibid.

[31]C.T. Atkinson "British Strategy and Battles in Westphalian Campaigns of 1758-1762." In *Journal of the United Services Institution.* p. 79, p. 516 (1934): 739-40.

[32]Ewald, *Diary*, p. xxv.

[33] Carl von Ewald Johannes *Ewald: Bilder aus dem Leben eines Soldaten.* Staatarchiv Kassel, Best. C19 Nr. 7217,4.

[34]Ewlad, *Gedanken*, pp. 1-6.

[35]On this point, see Robert S. Quimby, *The Background of Napoleonic Warfare: The Theory of Military Tactics in Eighteenth-Century France.* New York: Columbia University Press, 1957, pp. 16-7.

[36] Peter Paret, *Clausewitz and the State: The Man, his Theories, and his Times.* Princeton: Princeton University Press, 1985, pp. 191-92.

[37]Full bibliographic information on these works is as follows: *Johann von Ewald Gesprache eines Husarencorporals, eines Jagers und liechten Infanteristen uber die Pflichten und den Dienst der liechten Soldaten.* Altona: Hammerich, 1794. Johann von Ewald *Belehrunger uber den Kreig, besonders uber den kleinen Krieg, durch Beispiele grosser Helden und kluger und tapferer Manner.* 3 vols. Schleswig: J.G. Schlooss, 1798.

[38]Ewald, *Diary*, pp. xiv-v.

[39]Ewald is referring to Jacques-Francois de Chastenet, Marquis de Puysegur (1655-1743). Puysegur began his career as an officer in the French Regiment du Roi. He gained expertise in campaigning. He specialties were logistics and specifically the sighting of army camps, which he advised the Duke of Luxembourg on during the War of the Spanish Succession (1701-1715). His principle work, published posthumously, was *The Art of War*, where, in true Enlightenment fashion, he attempted to set out a set of rules and principles for the conduct of war. See Robert S. Quimby, *The Background of Napoleonic Warfare: The Theory of Military Tactics in Eighteenth-Century France.* New York: Columbia University Press, 1957, 16-7. See also Toby McCleod, "Puysegur, Jacques-Francois de Chastenent, Marquis de" in *Daniel Coet-*

*zee, and Lee Eystrulid eds. Philosophers of War The Evolution of History's Greatest Military Thinkers.* vol. 1, Santa Barbara, CA: Praeger, 2013, 313-4.

[40]Lieutenant General Lancelot Turpin de Comte de Crisse (1716-1795) Crisse began his service in the French army in a Hussar regiment. With the end of the War of the Austrian Succession, he achieved the rank of brigadier general. He saw extensive service in Germany in the Seven Years' War. Considered a philosophe, he wrote on a wide variety of subjects. His military ideas are to be found in the two-volume set *Essai sur l'art de la guerre* published between 1754 and 1757. He advocated the idea that the warfare was a science, which could be understood through intense study and the quality of genius. Crisse's *Essai* was translated into a number of languages during his lifetime and became a standard text for a generation of officers and military thinkers.

[41]Ewald is discussing the work of Sir La Cointe. This is M. Jean Louis Le Cointe *The Science of Military Posts: for the use of regimental officers who frequently command detached parties. In which is shewn the manner of attacking and defending posts. With cuts, explaining the Construction of Field Forts, and Intrenchment. By M. La Cointe of the Royal Academy at Nismes. To which are added some remarks taken from M. Saxe, De La Croix and others serving to the same purpose.* Translated from the French. By an officer. London: Printed for T. Payne, at the Mews Gate, 1761. Little biographical information is available on the officer. The work was initially published in French in 1759. In a recent article in the Journal of the American Revolution, Don N. Hagist noted that this was one of the key French works on the Art of War listed in George Smith's *An Universal Military Dictionary* under the entry "Books." See Don N. Hagist "The Military Library." in *Journal of the American Revolution,* November 17, 2014. Internet. https://allthingsliberty.com/2014/11/the-military-library/ Last accessed August 2, 2016. Based on the title, the work was clearly in line with what Ewald sought to discuss.

[42]The preceding remark may indicate that by now Ewald had learned to at least read French.

[43]Referring to Henry of Navarre (1553-1610) who later became Henry IV of France (r. 1589-1610). While a leader of the Huguenot resistance against the French crown, he often resorted to irregular tactics.

[44] It would seem here that Ewald was referring to Robert Cecil, First Earl of Salisbury (1563-1612), who played a significant role in putting

down the Irish Rebellion against English rule that occurred during the Nine Years' War (1688-97). See Alan Haynes, Robert Cecil, First *Earl of Salisbury: Servant of Two Sovereigns*. London: P. Owen, 1989.

[45]Four of the more well-known commanders of light troops from the Seven Years' War from the western European theater. They were: Nickolaus, Graf von Lückner, Colonel Heinrich Wilhelm von Freytag, Colonel Johann Christian Fischer, and Colonel von Scheiter. The exploits of all of these men are described, in varying detail in Savory, *His Britannic Majesty's Army*.

[46]Jean Charles, Chevalier de Folard (1669-1752) Folard was probably the most celebrated and debated military writer of the first half of the eighteenth century, not least for his ongoing debate with Puységur. Ewald would certainly have found a kindred spirit and possibly an idle in Folard who joined the French army at 16, after attending a Jesuit college. Folard fought in various battles of the War of Spanish Succession in Italy, and kept a notebook of his experiences and his thoughts on the conduct of war. These eventually came into print in his *Abrégé des commentaries de M. de Folard sur L'Histoire de Polybe (Commentaries on Polbus)*. The most recent biography of Folard as of this writing is *Jean Chagnoit Le Chavlier de Folard: Le Strategie d'incertitude*. Paris: Editions du Rocher, 1997. For more in-depth discussion of Folard's ideas, see Azar Gat, *The Origins of Military Thought: From the Enlightenment to Clausewitz*. Oxford: Clarendon Press, 1989; Brent Nosworthy *The Anatomy of Victory: Battle Tactics 1689-1763*. New York: Hippocrene Books, 1990; and Robert S. Quimby, *The Background of Napoleonic Warfare: The Theory of Military Tactics in Eighteenth-Century France*. New York: Columbia University Press, 1957.

[47]Johann Gottlieb von Rall (c. 1720-1776) was born in Hesse-Kassel and served in the Seven Years' War. He was given command of one of the newly raised Jäger companies during that conflict. In addition, Rall served in the Russian army against the Turks in their conflict of 1768-74. He returned to Hesse-Kassel and came to America at the age of 55. He holds the ignominious distinction of commanding the Hessian contingent that was surprised at Trenton on December 26, 1776, an engagement in which he was mortally wounded. For biographical information on Rall, see Boatner, *Enclyclopedia*, 911.

[48]Men would only march with their rifles inverted if they were certain they were moving through an area with relative impunity. As to seeing orders, in the field, orders were often transmitted to Jägers through the use of various hand signals. This method, obviously,

generated less noise than spoken orders or the use of hunting horns.

Friedrich Herman von Schonberg holds the curious distinction of being a marshal of France and a general in the English and Portuguese armies at different times, He died at the battle of the Boyne on July 1, 1690. The episode used as an example by Ewald occurred during Schomberg's service with the English during the *Portuguese Restoration War, 1640-1668*. See Matther Glozier, *Marshal Schomberg, 1615–1690: the ablest soldier of his age: international soldiering and the formation of state armies in seventeenth–century Europe*. Brighton: Sussex Academy Press, 2005.

[49]Falles served as Marshall Schomberg's French liaison on this part of the campaign

[50]Translator's note: These actions took place during Schomberg's service to France during the Portuguese Restoration War, a conflict in which France supported Spain. Schomberg commanded a 3,000 man force of English ex-patriots in this conflict.

[51]If the defenders within the structure begin firing too early, they would alert an opponent to their presence, and likely waste a good deal of powder. The latter stands as the more dangerous possibility, since no resupply would be forthcoming.

[52]In the original, Ewald uses the term *Fußbanke* for banquette. This literally renders as foot embankment, likely noting a very low defensive work.

[53]Translator's note, see Figure 2 at the end of this translation.

[54]Ewald is referring to the Johann Gottlieb Tielke whose work, *The Field Engineer or, Instruction upon every Branch of Field Fortification: Demonstrated by Examples which Occurred in the Seven Years' War between the Prussians, The Austrians and the Russians.* London: J. Walter, 1769. Ewald clearly read and found quite useful. Likewise, it should be clear form the groups mention in Tielke's title that he concerned himself primarily with the eastern theater of the war, which Ewald had not participated in.

[55]When he uses the term wretched war in the preceding paragraph, Ewald is referring to the Seven Years' War. One specific examples of this sort of defense occurred at the battle of the Amoneburg, in which Ewald participated.

[56]Here, Ewald is referring to the battle of Vellinghausen, also rendered as Villinghausen of Willinghausen, fought on July 15-16, 1761 between His Britannic Majesty's Army and a larger French army under the command of French marshals Duc de Broglie and Prince de Soubise.

[57]It seems here that Ewald is referring to the death of French lieutenant-general Pierre-François, Marquess of Rougé.

[58]This reference pertains to the fighting at the battle of Brücker Muhle, also known as Amöneburg, fought on September 21, 1762. This engagement was the last one in which Ewald saw combat during the Seven Years' War.

[59]Spartan king.

[60]Editor's note: It seems in this point, Ewald is confusing the Moors, North African Muslims, with Persians.

[61]This refers to King Porus, a monarch of the ancient Punjab reputed to have been defeated by Alexander the Great

[62]The inference here seems to be that if the attacking officer has a good deal of money, it would be more possible to bribe the commander of the fort and thus take it through those means.

[63]Translator's note, the chaff-mines Ewald speaks of were false mines dug to confuse the enemy when attacking a fortified post.

[64]A forlorn hope was a small advanced squad exposed to the most dangerous situations.

[65]Here, Ewald seems to be referring to an explosive device whose purpose was to blind the defenders with its flash when detonated. It would be similar in function to today's "flash-bang" devices.

[66]Translators note: Folard actually suggests the use of pikes and phalanxes for this sort of action. I have left the translation here closer to Ewald's original, which is "Sensen und Spontons" in order to preserve some of the feel of his text. It provides some insight on how Ewald understood Folard.

[67]Translator's note: partisans were long pole-arms with blades attached to one side. These weapons were advocated by Folard.

[68]Louis de Conflans, marquis de Armentières, (1711-1774) A French general and later marshal of France. During this period of the Seven Years' War, he served as a lieutenant general under marshals de Soubise and de Contades.

[69]Here, Ewald is referring to an incident in the Seven Years' War

[70]This was Johann Christian Fischer, who commanded a French partisan unit, see Savory, His Britannic Majesty's Army, 22, 53.

[71]In this particular passage, what Ewald seems to be alluding to is the notion that by attacking at night, or in the heat of the day, you do the unexpected, which brings fear to the enemy, thus acting as a force multiplier.

[72]The commander Folard is referring to is Maurice de Saxe.

[73]Count Felix Friedrich von Flemming (1661–1739), Prussian privy councilor for Friedrich I (r. 1688-1713).

[74]Also spelled Gontran, Guntram, Gunthchram, and Guntramnus, king of Burgundy (r. 561-592). After a siege of the city of Comminges, which occurred in 584 or 585 A.D., Gontram had his enemy, whom he had besieged in the town, executed. It is this event which seems to have drawn on him the criticism Ewald mentions. See St. Gregory of Tours. *The History of the Franks, Volume II*: Text. Trans. by Ormonde Maddock Dalton. Clarendon Press: 1967.

[75]A petard was a charge of gunpowder packed into a bell-shaped metal container. It would then be mounted on the gate of a town with the open end affixed to the gate, and detonated. The purpose of the device, like the modern shaped charge, was to blast in the gate to allow a storming party through the gate. These were still in production in the eighteenth century, though their use had dropped off.

[76]Here, Ewald is quoting from Guilliame Le Blond (1704-1781), a professor of mathematics and tutor to the children of louis XV. Le Blond possessed no personal military experience, but he did carefully draw on the works of experienced military writers, whom he cited. He was a contributor the *Encyclopedie* of Diderot on military matters, as well as publishing some seven works in his own right.

[77]This concerns a very tactical use of branches in order to create the deception that the obstacles are much more formidable than they truly are.

[78]Ewald is referring here to his own experience in the Seven Years' War.

[79]See plan II, page 66

[80] Ewald here uses the French term "peleton" in the original.

[81]See Plan III, page 67.

[82]Here, Ewald refers to the time of during which only the shepherds are awake so as to be able to lead their flocks out to grazing areas.

[83]Here Ewald might be referring to the Viking warriors known as berserks who flung themselves recklessly on their opponents.

[84]What Ewald seems to be discussing here is the tactic of forming square, which was often employed by infantry as a defense against cavalry.

[85]Flankers, soldiers who provided security on the flanks of a marching column.

[86]Ewald here clearly means that the battalion is subdivided. His peletons are akin to platoons and is rendered as such.

[87]In the original, Ewald uses the terms Flanquen, Tête, and queue. This could mean that he was relying heavily on French works in his writing on the topic.

[88]Ewald seems to be describing the deployment of the battalion columns so that they march in echelon.

[89]The following events occurred during the War of the Polish Succession (1733-38)

[90]Here again, Ewald is referring to his own recent experiences in the Seven Years' War.

# About the Author

Jim Mc Intyre received his Bachelors in History from Temple University in 1996 and his Masters from the University of Illinois in 1999. His main interest is the American War of Independence, on which he has written numerous articles and papers. He is the author of *The Development of the British Light Infantry, Continental and North American Influences 1740-1765* and *Johann Ewald: Partisan Commander*. He teaches History at Moraine Valley Community College near Chicago, Illinois and serves as a Fleet Professor in the United States Naval War College's College of Distance Education, Strategy and War Department as well.

# Index

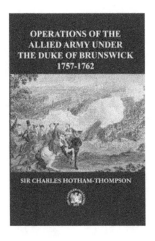